Foreword

In December 2000 the Government published the White Paper *Reforming the Mental Health Act*, which set out proposals for managing the small number of individuals considered dangerous as a result of a severe personality disorder.

An essential component of the Government's strategy is to increase the evidence base to help inform the development of beneficial interventions for this group. With this aim in mind, this report provides a comprehensive review of the literature concerning interventions aimed at adolescents at risk for developing a clinical diagnosis of severe antisocial personality disorder in adulthood (ASPD).

The review considers the definition and measurement of ASPD, risk factors for its development, the timing and nature of interventions and the evidence in support of various forms of intervention.

However, this review demonstrates that there are still significant gaps in our knowledge about the causes of severe antisocial personality disorders. In order to address such gaps the joint Home Office, Department of Health and Prison Service programme on Dangerousness and Severe Personality Disorder has established a major programme of research. As such this review provides a basis for directing the research effort.

Chris Lewis
Head of Offenders and Corrections Unit
Research Development and Statistics Directorate
Home Office
September 2001

Acknowledgements

This report is the result of a literature review funded by the Home Office. We are grateful to the Home Office, and Dr Dilys Jones in particular, for support throughout the short but intense life of the project. We are also grateful to members of the Mental Health Unit for their assistance, and to the members of the project's Steering Group who gave feedback at various stages of the report. The Steering Group members were: Sarah Casemore, George Goodwin, Bob Jezzard, Dilys Jones, Robert Newman, Jonathan Sedgwick, Nicole Smith, and Gail Winter.

In addition, because of the short timetable for the review, we have relied on informal advice, comments and direction from a number of experts in this field, including: Susan Bailey, Geoffrey Baruch, Ron Blackburn, James Blair, Len Bowers, Felicity Clarkson, Jeremy Coid, Jan Davis, Maria Duggan, David Farrington, Peter Fonagy, Michael Little, Michael Maher, Mary Piper, Jane Pooley, and John Shine.

Patricia Moran
Ann Hagell

Home Office Research Study 225

Intervening to prevent antisocial personality disorder:
a scoping review

Patricia Moran and Ann Hagell

Home Office Research, Development and Statistics Directorate
September 2001

Home Office Research Studies

The Home Office Research Studies are reports on research undertaken by or on behalf of the Home Office. They cover the range of subjects for which the Home Secretary has responsibility. Other publications produced by the Research, Development and Statistics Directorate include Findings, Statistical Bulletins and Statistical Papers.

The Research, Development and Statistics Directorate

RDS is part of the Home Office. The Home Office's purpose is to build a safe, just and tolerant society in which the rights and responsibilities of individuals, families and communities are properly balanced and the protection and security of the public are maintained.

RDS is also a part of the Government Statistical Service (GSS). One of the GSS aims is to inform Parliament and the citizen about the state of the nation and provide a window on the work and performance of government, allowing the impact of government policies and actions to be assessed.

Therefore -

Research Development and Statistics Directorate exists to improve policy making, decision taking and practice in support of the Home Office purpose and aims, to provide the public and Parliament with information necessary for informed debate and to publish information for future use.

First published 2001
Application for reproduction should be made to the Communications and Development Unit, Room 201, Home Office, 50 Queen Anne's Gate, London SW1H 9AT.
© Crown copyright 2001   ISBN   1 84082 705 X
                           ISSN   0072 6435

Contents

Summary

Background and introduction

This report is a scoping review of literature concerning interventions aimed at adolescents at risk of developing antisocial personality disorder (ASPD) in adulthood. The review was carried out by the Policy Research Bureau, and commissioned by the Mental Health Unit at the Home Office. It forms one part of the government's current activity aimed at developing policy and practice guidelines for managing the small number of individuals considered dangerous and severely personality disordered (DSPD). The present report focuses on ASPD rather than DSPD because at the present the latter category has no legal or clinical definition. Not all dangerous and severely personality disordered individuals will have a diagnosis of ASPD, but many will. Although ASPD in adulthood is rare, the significant danger posed by a minority of such individuals raises the need to consider preventative strategies for tackling the development of the disorder. The present report covers studies that consider ASPD as an outcome, but also draws on literature concerning related outcomes such as psychopathy, and violent or chronic offending. The report discusses issues concerning definition and measurement of ASPD, risk factors for its development, the timing and nature of interventions, the evidence in support of various forms of intervention, and finally, implications for future research, policy and practice.

Definitions

Definitions in the field of antisocial behaviour remain blurred. Terms such as psychopathy, antisocial personality disorder, dangerous and severely personality disordered are often used interchangeably, although they involve different clinical and legal criteria. There are a number of overlapping groups within the broad category of individuals with antisocial behaviour. Even those with the most severe antisocial behaviour are not necessarily a homogeneous group, and this has implications for their identification and treatment. Whilst antisocial behaviour is evident in about 30 per cent of adolescents, ASPD is diagnosable in approximately three per cent of adults. A group labelled dangerous and severely personality disordered (DSPD) includes possibly as few as 2,000 adults, according to official statistics (Home Office/Department of Health, 1999). Currently, DSPD is a term used for convenience and it is still undergoing clarification to establish its meaning in terms of clinical and/or legal criteria. More careful and precise use of terms is required so that we can target our interventions and treatment.

Risk factors: foci for prevention and intervention

A number of risk factors have been identified as predictive of ASPD in adulthood. These include many factors that are related to other disorders, and specificity of risk factors has yet to be discovered. Key factors in the development of ASPD appear to be early-onset, life-course persistent antisocial behaviour, co-morbid with attention-deficit/hyperactivity disorder. ASPD adults frequently have experienced severe neglect or abuse, and are likely to have been raised by parents or caregivers with their own psychiatric problems and difficulties in parenting. However, these risk factors are not unique to ASPD, and further investigation is required to achieve improved specificity.

Designing and evaluating interventions

In designing interventions, consideration needs to be given to the size of the target population, the choice of risk factors to tackle and the need for early or late intervention. With a low base rate for ASPD, any intervention is in danger of targeting a larger proportion of the population than will actually go on to develop the disorder, and this has implications for cost-effectiveness. Multiple interventions at multiple points throughout the life course may be required to overcome the problems of those at highest risk, beginning with broad community-based interventions and progressing to highly specific interventions for a small group who require more intensive input. The optimum type and frequency of interventions required to offset development of ASPD is not known.

Identifying high-risk adolescents

Not surprisingly, given the problems with establishing definitions and the lack of specificity of risk factors, a means of identifying high-risk adolescents has yet to be found. Currently, there is no specific tool or measure that has proven ability to pinpoint the very small number of individuals with the worst prognosis from amongst the six per cent of young people who have life-course persistent antisocial behaviour. Advances in the knowledge of risk factors may lead to the development of instruments for assessing client risk level, and therefore enable identification of those at highest risk who may require very specialist intervention. The consequence of poor ability to identify high-risk adolescents is that intensive and costly interventions may be targeted at a larger group than is necessary. Instruments must also be developed to assess the needs of the client group, so that the appropriateness of a particular intervention for a given client can be determined.

Research on interventions with adolescents

Interventions with adolescents show limited results in terms of long-term outcome. There is little conclusive evidence regarding the effectiveness of any single intervention over time, although short-term results may show promise. This result relates to the inadequacy of evaluation studies as much as it does to the inadequacies of the interventions themselves. However, multi-modal, well-structured, intensive, lengthy programmes that are cognitive-behavioural in orientation are the types of intervention most likely to impact on adolescents with very disturbed or difficult behaviour. Interventions that are closely tailored to characteristics of the individual may be more successful than broader, population-based strategies.

Conclusions and policy implications

There are substantial gaps in our understanding of ASPD, and of interventions that may prevent its development. This lack of knowledge seriously hampers the formation of policy guidelines aimed at prevention of ASPD. However, if future research is directed at a number of key areas, we can begin to develop and deliver programmes that may reduce the likelihood of young people developing ASPD or else improve the functioning of those on a pathway to development of the disorder. Priorities for future research include developing terminology, diagnoses and classification systems, both in the clinical and the legal context. This will enable us, for example, to capitalise on research by pooling results across studies. A second area for future research is the need to establish patterns and trends in terms of, for example, the rates of disorder found in different populations of young people in a variety of contexts. A third area in which knowledge is lacking is the aetiology of ASPD. Understanding the developmental pathways involved in ASPD will help to inform future interventions by identifying both the characteristics of the group most at risk, and also the risk and protective factors that should be addressed by the intervention. Finally, evaluation of interventions needs to take place in a scientifically rigorous manner, in order to establish which type of interventions work best, under what circumstances, and for whom. Such research will also enable us to develop clearer understanding of the requirements for multi-disciplinary working to meet the complex needs of high-risk groups, and to develop appropriate professional (and other) training and supervision for staff.

1   **Introduction**

Background

Most adolescents have problems of some description. Most adolescents, certainly most boys, will behave in an antisocial way. The behaviour is mainly limited to adolescence, but for a minority it will be what Moffitt (1993) calls life-course-persistent, with manifestations noted in childhood and evident well into adulthood. Some of those with enduring patterns of antisocial behaviour will be diagnosed in adulthood (using internationally recognised classification systems) as having personality disorders, one of which is antisocial personality disorder or ASPD.

Adults with ASPD represent a potentially very dangerous group. The most dangerous in this group are few in number, probably no more than 2,000 at any one time (Home Office/Department of Health, 1999). Most are locked up in prison or detained in mental health institutions, but a small number, estimated to be around 300 to 600, are managed in the community.

This review is concerned with the prevention of ASPD by activities directed at adolescents who behave in an antisocial way or with the smaller group of life-course-persistent offenders or with those who display other forms of personality disorder. The policy context for this review is clear: the government has recently issued proposals to develop policies to manage dangerous people with severe personality disorders (Home Office/Department of Health, 2000). Although severe personality disorders are rare, adults with such disorders may pose a high risk to the public. Prevention has been identified as part of the overall strategy needed to tackle the issue. There is thus a need to appraise what is known about these disorders and what can be done early on to prevent their development.

Research aims

The aim of this report is to review the available literature in order to answer the following questions:
1. What is antisocial personality disorder?
2. What is known about the developmental pathways and risk factors leading to the disorder?

3. Is it possible to identify adolescents at high risk of ASPD in adulthood?
4. What interventions with adolescents are successful in preventing progression to ASPD in adulthood?
5. What are the implications of these findings for future research, policy and service provision?

The available literature is not vast, yet it encompasses a diversity of theoretical and methodological approaches, and is spread across a range of disciplines, including psychiatry, psychology, law, criminology and social work.

The report has been focussed on material concerning the identification of the most effective interventions. Extended theoretical debate about risk factors was avoided unless it was directly relevant to existing or potential interventions. Such discussions have been dealt with at length in other reviews (e.g. Farrington, 1995; Paul Moran, 1999[1]; Rutter, Giller, & Hagell, 1998; Stoff, Breiling, & Maser, 1997).

Methods

The review involved systematic searches of literature for information regarding risk factors for severe personality disorder and interventions with adolescents. This included articles, books and reports concerned with forensic and adolescent psychiatry, mental health and social services.

Sources of literature

The first stage of the review involved mapping out the relevant key issues. Subsequently, a number of databases were searched for relevant published and unpublished material. These included PsycLit, Medline, and BIDS. In addition, several journals were searched by hand to locate relevant articles not identified through database searches, and also to locate recently published work that had not yet been indexed. The on-line catalogues of the Cochrane Library and also the Library of Congress were searched, as well as the SIGLE grey literature database, and Inside Web via the British Library. Reports were also downloaded from the Virtual Institute for Severe Personality Disorder (VISPED) website. A number of Internet search engines were also used to locate information published via the Internet, including SOSIG and BUBL.

---

1.   We have referred to Paul Moran using his full name to distinguish him from the first author of this report.

The search predominantly identified studies from the US and UK, carried out in the last three decades. During this time a number of influential longitudinal studies were underway, including the Cambridge Study in Delinquent Development (West & Farrington, 1973, 1977), the Newcastle Thousand Family Study (Kolvin et al, 1990), the Dunedin study in New Zealand (Moffit & Silva, 1988), and American studies such as Robins (1979), to name but a few.

Given the limitations in the literature, a number of experts were consulted to explore ongoing projects that had not reached the final stages of publication. They included treatment providers such as therapists, adolescent forensic psychiatrists, and adult psychiatrists, as well as youth offending and juvenile justice policy makers, and researchers in the areas of delinquency and treatment of difficult and disturbed young people. These people are listed in the acknowledgements.

Inclusion criteria

Even within the limited relevant literature, it was necessary to establish inclusion criteria. Studies were included that encompassed a broader range of outcomes than ASPD, such as offending. A delicate balancing act had to be achieved to ensure the criteria for inclusion were neither too strict nor too lax. If extremely stringent criteria had been applied to include only methodologically robust studies, then there would have been very little to report on. On the other hand, by broadening the criteria to allow studies with methodological weaknesses, the report would be danger of becoming over-inclusive and unfocused. Therefore, wherever possible, studies have been included from broader areas (such as antisocial behaviour) only when there is specific mention of samples with particularly severe antisocial behaviour or extremely poor prognosis. Studies with methodological weaknesses (for example, lacking a comparison group, or poor sample definition) have been included only when they represent the only known evaluation of a particular intervention, and attention is drawn to the limitations of the results.

Structure of the report

The report begins with definitions of adolescence, antisocial behaviour and antisocial personality disorder. ASPD is put in the context of other personality disorders as well as broader categories of antisocial behaviour. Next, the literature concerning risk factors for antisocial personality disorder is reviewed, focusing on those most likely to form the target of intervention programmes. This is followed by a discussion of the design of successful interventions, including the risk factors they tackle, the scale of the intervention and its target group, and the timing of the intervention relative to risks arising across the life course. The tasks of assessing risk and identifying high-risk adolescents for intervention are then discussed. The interventions are then described. Finally, the conclusions from this review of the literature are drawn together to address the implications for research, policy and practice.

Introduction

This report concerns working with adolescents to prevent the onset of ASPD in adulthood. Much of the focus falls on young people in their mid to late teens who are showing the first signs of what may become ASPD. We begin by considering definitions of the various terms to be used throughout the report, starting with a discussion of the nature of adolescence. We then move on to a discussion of antisocial behaviour, and within this context we define various overlapping sub-groups. These include the relatively small group of adults with ASPD and other personality disorders, and the even smaller group defined as dangerous and severely personality disordered.

Adolescence as a developmental stage

Adolescents account for approximately seven million people in the UK (1996 figures, Coleman, 1999). As a life stage, adolescence is usually defined as beginning at the onset of puberty and ending when physical growth ceases or almost ceases. This typically covers an age range of 13 to 18 years (Furnham & Gunter, 1989) although some writers use a longer period (e.g. 10 to 19 years, Coleman & Hendry, 1999). Adolescence is marked by significant shifts in character and social development, and there are several perspectives from which to view these transitions, including 'psychosexual development, ego development and defensive operations, identity formation, cognitive development, object relations and more latterly self-psychology' (p20; Bailey, 1996). There are a number of useful reviews of the general literature in this area (e.g. Coleman & Hendry, 1999).

Early descriptions of adolescence emphasised rebelliousness and unpredictable behaviour (Freud, 1958; Hall, 1904) or identity crisis (Erikson, 1968). More latterly such 'turmoil' theories have been questioned, as large-scale surveys have revealed that four out of five adolescents function well and have stable relationships with their family and friends (Offer, Ostrov, & Howard, 1981; Rutter & Rutter, 1993). However, it is still said that the nature of adolescence 'is to act, and to act instantly' (Villani & Sharfstein, 1999) and clearly the period presents major personal challenges. To make the transition from adolescence to adulthood, the individual must learn 'inhibition of action and reaction' (Hay, Castle and Jewett, 1994). Hence adolescence represents a key stage in development that may result in poor functioning in adulthood if not negotiated successfully.

Many of the features of adolescence – transitions from school to work, from dependence to independence, from the sphere of family life to the world of peer influences – also create challenges for assessment, prevention and intervention with this age group. In a review of adolescent services, Steinberg wrote:

> 'All of the broad groups of conditions seen in the whole of psychiatry may also be encountered in adolescence; however, the developmental changes of this period result in the clinical phenomena of this age group being sometimes less clear and more variable than those seen in older patients...What is peculiar to adolescence, and the ambiguous and changing position each boy or girl occupies between say, 10 and 20, is the existence of a moral, legal and social potential space into which any number of people may step and claim authority...'
> (p1006; Steinberg, 1994).

However, it is also important to be reminded that age can be a 'non-explanation' (Rutter & Rutter, 1993) and we should avoid being rigid about the boundaries of the adolescence age range. Some people outside the age range may have more in common with some adolescents than the communality shared by any one set of adolescents.

In order to identify adolescents in need of intervention, it is important to understand what is considered as 'normal' functioning and good mental health in young people. A recent definition put forward the following criteria:

- a capacity to enter into and sustain mutually satisfying personal relationships

- continuing progression of psychological development

- an ability to play and learn so that attainments are appropriate for age and intellectual level

- a developing moral sense of right and wrong

- the degree of psychological distress and maladaptive behaviour being within the normal limits for the child's age and context.
                                                          (NHS/Health Advisory Service, 1995)

It is clear that these goals may not be attained by everybody: approximately 15 per cent of adolescents meet the criteria for psychiatric disorder in any one-year period (e.g. Steinberg,

1994), and for some the disorder may develop a chronic course, persisting into adulthood. This may be due in part to the various risks encountered along the developmental pathway, which are reviewed in Chapter 3.

Antisocial behaviour in adolescents

ASPD in adulthood is a disorder that, in most cases, emerges from antisocial behaviour in adolescence. Whilst recent research suggests that severe antisocial behaviour may emerge in adulthood without a childhood history of such behaviour (e.g. Tweed et al, 1994), the current report focuses primarily on ASPD that has been preceded by antisocial behaviour in childhood. This is because the current report concerns ways in which to intervene with adolescents who show early risk for later ASPD, and relatively little is known about antecedent risk factors for development of adult-onset ASPD.

There are several recent reviews on antisocial behaviour and the related concept of conduct disorder (Rutter et al, 1998; Stoff et al, 1997). It is clear from these that at least some types of antisocial behaviour are virtually normative in males. Self-report data suggest that somewhere between 50 and 90 per cent of young men engage in behaviour that involves breaking the law, whether or not prosecution takes place. Home Office figures show that 34 per cent of adult men have acquired a criminal record by their 40s (Home Office, 1998). Antisocial behaviour in young women is less common but still not infrequent. Home Office estimates show that by their 40s approximately eight per cent of women have a criminal record. The types of antisocial behaviour accounted for in these actions are well-documented (Rutter et al, 1998; Rutter & Smith, 1995; Graham & Bowling, 1995). It mostly consists of theft and, for young men, car-related crime. It is important to note that 'antisocial' is not synonymous with 'criminal' behaviour, since some forms of antisocial behaviour are not illegal, e.g. defaulting on promises, or lying. Neither is 'antisocial' synonymous with 'dangerous', since much antisocial behaviour is not directly dangerous to anyone.

There is much heterogeneity in antisocial behaviour (Rutter et al, 1998). At the risk of grossly oversimplifying, much of the available research evidence from longitudinal studies leads to the conclusion that two main sub-groups can be delineated. The more common group involves 'adolescent-limited' antisocial behaviour displayed by around a quarter or more of the general population, predominantly males (Moffitt, 1993; Moffitt et al, 1996). In this group, the behaviour does not set in until adolescence, and generally does not persist into adulthood. In contrast, a second group of individuals continue to commit antisocial acts from early childhood into adulthood, and are thus labelled 'life-course persistent' (Moffitt, 1993).

Estimates of prevalence for life-course persistent antisocial behaviour in the general population are in the region of six per cent (Kratzer & Hodgins, 1996; Moffitt et al, 1996). There is general acceptance in the literature that these two groups have significance for prediction of outcomes for troubled adolescents, although it is widely accepted that that there may be other groups. As described earlier, there is evidence to suggest that there may be an adult-onset group who shows no antisocial behaviour in childhood (Tweed et al, 1994). In future much more will become known about these various categories as participants in longitudinal research projects get older. Moffitt's series, for example, had only just reached early adulthood by the late 1990s.

Personality disorder in adulthood

Personality is something that people have, not something (like antisocial behaviour) that they do, although personality dispositions are inferred from behaviour. There is a long and rich research tradition in the whole area of personality formation and functioning, and a smaller, specialised literature on personalities that 'go wrong'. The notion of 'personality' itself has been at the heart of the underlying theoretical assumptions of psychology, which has swung back and forth over the previous century between believing that all the explanations for behaviour lay in personality, to believing that studying and understanding behaviour was the only way to learn about the human condition.

Personality disorders are reflected in an individual's cognitive processing, and affect regulation, interpersonal functioning and impulse control. They have been described as the 'Achilles' heel of psychiatry' (Prins, 1991). They are difficult to diagnose and they are consequently difficult to treat

Despite advances in international classification systems described below, the clinical diagnosis of personality disorders frequently fails to meet psychometric requirements of reliability and validity. The categories identified seldom represent distinct syndromes (Blackburn, 2000). However, most experts agree that personality disorders are, in the words of one set of reviewers, '...pervasive and persistent abnormalities of overall personality functioning that cause social impairment and/or subjective distress, but that are not due to episodic disorders of mental state, and that are not the result of qualitatively disordered thought processes...' (p688; Hill & Rutter, 1994).

Disordered personality types are delineated in clinical diagnostic systems such as the DSM-IV scheme of the American Psychiatric Association (1994), and the ICD-10 scheme of the

World Health Organisation (1993). Within these diagnostic schemes personality disorders include: antisocial, paranoid, schizoid, schizotypal, obsessive-compulsive, histrionic, dependent, narcissistic, avoidant, passive, anxious, borderline and impulsive. A diagnosis of personality disorder cannot be made until an individual has reached adulthood. However, there is some evidence for the validity of borderline disorder in children (Greenman et al, 1986), and 'complex post-traumatic stress disorder' has also been proposed (Herman, 1992).

A diagnosis of personality disorder is usually made by a mental health professional, commonly a psychiatrist. However, the diagnosis does not imply a mental illness. Both of the major classification systems distinguish between mental disorders such as depression (on Axis I of DSM-IV) and personality disorders (on Axis II of DSM-IV). These in turn have to be distinguished from mental illness, implying some distortion of thought or perception. As we shall see, there is considerable co-morbidity between personality disorders, some co-morbidity between personality and mental disorders, and a little overlap between personality disorders and mental illness.

The prevalence rate for personality disorders differs according to the diagnostic criteria applied, and method of assessment. Furthermore, few studies examine the full range of personality disorders. Surveys indicate that lifetime rates for personality disorders such as paranoid, schizoid, and narcissistic personality disorders vary between one per cent (Coid, 1998) and five per cent (Samuels et al, 1994). Studies of patients in psychiatric settings show that many personality disordered individuals have disorders in more than one diagnostic category (Morey, 1988; Stuart et al, 1998). Not only are personality disorders co-morbid both with other Axis II disorders, there is also overlap with Axis I disorders. The overlap between categories of personality disorder is reported to be very high, for example, 99 per cent in some cases between antisocial and borderline categories (Blackburn, 2000). Many dangerous offenders have been found to have recurring patterns of co-varying traits rather than a single category of personality disorder (Blackburn & Coid, 1999).

Antisocial personality disorder (ASPD)

ASPD is one of ten different types of personality disorder on Axis II of the DSM-IV classification system. The diagnosis requires behaviour problems in childhood as well as persistent features in adulthood. As such they are extreme representatives of the group described above as showing antisocial behaviour, and would fall exclusively within the life-course persistent group. According to DSM-IV criteria, ASPD is a pervasive pattern of disregard for and violation of the rights of others. It encompasses a range of behaviours and traits including committing unlawful acts, deceitfulness, impulsiveness, a failure to plan ahead, aggressiveness, recklessness, and a lack of remorse. To fulfil the diagnostic criteria the individual must be at least 18 years of age, and also have had conduct disorder with onset before the age of 15. The WHO classification (ICD-10) uses different language but similar criteria. According to ICD-10, ASPD is referred to as dyssocial personality disorder. It is characterised by a callous unconcern for the feelings of others, gross and persistent irresponsibility, inability to maintain enduring relationships, low tolerance for frustration and low threshold for discharge of aggression, incapacity to experience guilt or to profit from experience, and proneness to blame others.

Prevalence of and co-morbidity in ASPD

Studies from the US and Europe indicate that the lifetime prevalence for ASPD is between one and three per cent in the general population (e.g. Robins & Regier, 1991; Paul Moran, 1999). A large cross-sectional survey of 18,571 Americans, for example, assessed respondents in institutions as well as private households (the Epidemiological Catchment Area Study; EDA) and reported a lifetime prevalence rate for ASPD of 2.4 per cent (Robins & Regier, 1991). The more recent National Co-morbidity Survey, assessing psychiatric disorder against DSM-IIIR criteria and by means of structured psychiatric interview in 8,098 non-institutionalised Americans, reported a similar lifetime rate of 3.5 per cent (Kessler et al, 1994). When compared to other psychiatric conditions, therefore, ASPD is rare. The same study reported, for example, 17.1 per cent prevalence for major depression, 24.9 per cent for anxiety, and 26.6 per cent for substance abuse/dependence.

Within prison populations in the UK, personality disorder prevalence rates are reported to be much greater, especially amongst offenders serving long sentences (Coid, 1992, 1998). A recent government survey of psychiatric morbidity among prisoners in England and Wales revealed that ASPD had the highest prevalence of any category of personality disorder (Singleton et al, 1998). Clinical interviews conducted on a sub-sample of prisoners showed that 49 per cent of male prisoners and 31 per cent of female prisoners were diagnosed as having ASPD.

Gender differences in rates of disorder are reported for ASPD, but there are few studies of gender differences regarding other personality disorders. Higher rates of ASPD are generally recorded in male samples, with one study reporting a ratio of 8:1 (Swanson, Bland & Newman, 1994). In terms of symptom profile, a study of antisocial personality disordered individuals attending a residential treatment programme found that in childhood, females were more likely than males to have run away, but less likely to have used weapons in fights, been cruel to animals, carried out acts of vandalism or set fires. In adulthood, the women had more often been irresponsible financially and as parents, engaged in prostitution, been violent towards partners and children, failed to plan ahead, and lacked remorse (Goldstein et al, 1996).

In relation to ethnicity, a survey of incarcerated American males indicated that a diagnosis of ASPD was applied more often to black rather than white inmates (Stevens, 1993). Similarly, a study of insanity acquittees in Missouri found that African American males were more likely than Caucasians to have a diagnosis of antisocial personality disorder, as well as of substance abuse and schizophrenia (Linhorst, Hunsucker, & Parker, 1998). However, these findings are contradicted by another study of male prison inmates which found that whites were more likely than non-whites to receive diagnoses of ASPD and substance abuse (Collins, Schlenger, & Jordan, 1988). Results from a UK survey of prisoners indicates that whilst black prisoners were less likely than white prisoners to have a diagnosis of personality disorder, black prisoners who were born in the UK were more likely to receive such a diagnosis (Singleton et al, 1998). Surveys of the general population are more consistent in their results. Paul Moran (1999) reports on a number of general population studies which show that no significant differences have been found in rates of antisocial personality disorder when black and non-black groups have been compared.

In terms of other demographic indicators, ASPD is associated with low educational attainment (Robins, Tipp, & Przybeck, 1991), a particularly high rate of unemployment (Bland et al, 1988), job instability, low job status (Farrington, 1991), and being unmarried (Barry et al, 1997). Higher rates of ASPD have been found amongst unmarried, separated and divorced individuals, and the lowest rates have been found amongst those who are married (Bland, Orn, & Newman, 1988).

Turning to co-morbidity, in terms of Axis I disorders, substance abuse often co-occurs with ASPD (Blackburn & Coid, 1999; Rounsaville et al, 1998; Swanson et al, 1994). A recent study of alcoholic men living in the community showed that ASPD was associated with earlier age of first intoxication, a more chronic and severe course of alcoholism, more adverse social consequences of drinking, and higher levels of drug use (Holdcraft, Iacono, & McGue, 1998). These findings confirm those reported a decade earlier by Yates, Petty, and Brown (1988) amongst a group of male alcoholics in treatment. Results from a study of 151 violent offenders aged 14-29 for whom ASPD was the primary disorder, showed that early onset of antisocial behaviour was associated with early onset of alcohol and drug abuse, and that these were risk factors for further violence (Daniel et al, 1983).

In addition to substance misuse, ASPD has been associated with suicidal behaviour (Dyck et al, 1988; Garvy & Spoden, 1980), depression (Sanderson et al, 1992), anxiety (Hoffart et al, 1994), and schizophrenia (Bland, Newman & Orn, 1987). The significance of co-morbidity in terms of common or distinct aetiological pathways remains unclear, and requires longitudinal studies to further understanding of the mechanisms involved.

How is ASPD measured?

Allied to the problems concerning definitions of ASPD are problems with its measurement. There is disparity in the range of features assessed by various instruments, with some placing emphasis on personality and others on behaviour (Lilienfeld, 1994). Commonly used measures include interviews such as the Structured Clinical Interview for DSM-III Axis II disorders (SCID; Spitzer & Williams, 1987) and questionnaires such as the Psychopathy Checklist Revised (PCL-R; Hare, 1991). Other sources of information include clinicians' ratings.

A review by Lilienfeld, Purcell and Jones-Alexander (1997) concludes that findings based on one self-report measure cannot necessarily be generalised to findings based on other self-report measures of ASPD. They also report that agreement between standardised interviews tends to be poor, as is diagnostic concordance between self-report and interview measures of ASPD. It is difficult, therefore, to draw conclusions across studies when different definitions and measures of personality disorder have been used. The question of how to assess early signs of ASPD is discussed in more detail in Chapter 5.

How does ASPD relate to 'psychopathy'?

Terms often used interchangeably with ASPD include psychopathy, psychopathic personality, or sociopathy. Cleckley (1941) was an early proponent of the term 'psychopath', used to denote a pattern of socially deviant behaviour and traits in adulthood. Psychopaths have been conceptualised as 'grandiose, arrogant, callous, superficial, and manipulative…short-tempered, unable to form strong emotional bonds with others, and lacking in empathy, guilt, or remorse . . . irresponsible, impulsive, and prone to violate social and legal norms and expectations' (p 22-23; Hart & Hare, 1997). Although criminality and violence are not part of the defining features of psychopathy, most of the research in this area has been carried out using offenders (Hare, 1970). Psychopathy overlaps with ASPD, although the overlap is asymmetrical. Hare (1985), for example, found that 90 per cent of psychopathic offenders met DSM-IIIR criteria for ASPD but only 25 per cent of those diagnosed as ASPD met criteria for psychopathy.

In English law the term 'psychopath' has also been used to encompass individuals who pose a danger to others, although in terms of clinical diagnostic categories of disorder, its meaning remains unclear. The Mental Health Act, 1983, describes psychopathic disorder as: 'A persistent disorder or disability of mind . . . which also results in abnormally aggressive or seriously irresponsible conduct on the part of the person concerned'. Coid's (1992) study of hospitalised subjects held under the Mental Health Act category of 'psychopathic disorder' found that only 31 per cent of women and 23 per cent of men rated as psychopaths according to a commonly used measure of psychopathy (PCL-R). Only 44 per cent of women and 38 per cent of men had a diagnosis of ASPD, and borderline personality disorder proved to be the most common diagnosis, rated for 91 per cent of women and 56 per cent of men.

Life course of ASPD

There appear to be more studies regarding the course of ASPD than of any other personality disorder. Swanson et al (1994) found that peak lifetime and six-month prevalence rates for ASPD occurred in the 25 to 34-year-old and 18 to 24-year-old age groups, respectively, and that lifetime rates dropped dramatically after age 34. In terms of other studies examining the duration of ASPD, the ECA study showed that average time from experience of first to last symptom was 19 years (Robins & Regier, 1991). A study by Black and others (1997) followed a group of 45 hospitalised men with ASPD, and found that older subjects who had been followed for longer were more likely to have improved, a result also reported by others (e.g. Harpur & Hare, 1994). This fall-off in diagnosis with age has also been reported among female samples. Daniel, Harris and Husain (1981) report that ASPD was the most common diagnosis amongst a sample of female offenders aged 17 to 39, whilst amongst those aged 40 to 45, there were no cases of ASPD.

The decline in ASPD prevalence with age may be due to a combination of the ageing process and effects of punishment leading to a 'burn-out' in the criminal drive, or else a psychological maturation involving redefinition of goals (Walters, 1990). Harpur and Hare (1994) suggest that impulsivity, social deviance and general antisocial behaviour may decline with age, but traits fundamental to psychopathy such as egocentricity, manipulativeness and callousness may endure.

'Dangerousness' and dangerous and severe personality disorders

Some ASPD involves more 'purposeful and destructive' forms of behaviour (Harris, Rice & Cormier, 1994), in which there is potential to harm both self and others. Reducing harm and the threat of harm is a central concern reflected in both current penal policy and recent legislation (Kemshall, 1996). A small number of potentially harmful individuals with personality disorders are known as 'dangerous severely personality disordered' (DSPD; Home Office/Department of Health, 1999). There are believed to be approximately 2,000 individuals who can be described as severely personality disordered and dangerous currently in the UK (Home Office/Department of Health, 1999). This figure is based in part on the findings of a survey by the Office for National Statistics carried out amongst prisoners in the UK (Singleton et al, 1998). It revealed that 1,400 men in prison fulfilled this description, and that a further 400 male patients detained in secure psychiatric hospitals were described as psychopathic (in legal rather than clinical terms). In addition, between 300 and 600 more men in the community are thought to fall into the DSPD category, although there are no current research data available on community prevalence (Home Office/Department of Health, 1999), but this is forthcoming.

DSPD as a term has (as yet) no recognition in legal or clinical fields. Its definition is, at the time of writing, being developed so that its inclusiveness of disorders such as ASPD or dyssocial personality disorders may become clearer. It is possible that some people display behaviours that pose a danger to both the public and the individual themselves, but which do not have any adolescent antisocial behaviour antecedents and cannot be diagnosed as ASPD. These people may have other personality disorders, for example, paranoid, narcissistic and borderline. Further work is underway to arrive at a satisfactory conceptualisation and measurement of DSPD so that policy affecting such individuals can be developed.

There are many problems in defining dangerousness and seriousness within an already high-risk group, and different definitions have been taken for different purposes. Dangerousness has been defined by Scott (1977) as an 'unpredictable and untreatable tendency to inflict or risk irreversible injury or destruction or to induce others to do so' (p128; Scott, 1977). Seriousness is often used to indicate 'more of' rather than 'qualitatively different' (Blackburn, 2000). Alternative ways of rating severity might include presence of co-morbid personality disorders or mental disorders, or by equating severity and dangerousness, so that the most severe are those who are most dangerous, or by focusing on severity of dysfunction rather than severity of symptoms (Blackburn, 2000).

Since the term DSPD is newly coined, there is currently no literature that specifically addresses this 'condition'. More common are reports of antisocial personality disordered individuals, psychopathic offenders, chronic violent offenders or delinquents. Whenever possible, studies have been selected for inclusion in the current report which specify personality disorders such as ASPD as their focus, and some of these individuals may be described as being dangerous and severely personality disordered. However, given the rarity of reports concerning interventions with ASPD, studies have sometimes been included that are concerned with closely related outcomes, where relevant. In such instances, the particular focus involved has been specified.

Conclusions

In this chapter we have attempted to describe the nature of adolescence and its relationship to antisocial behaviour, and to delineate various forms of antisocial behaviour ranging from adolescent-limited to the much rarer DSPD. As we have seen, the terms adolescent-limited antisocial behaviour, life-course persistent antisocial behaviour, personality disorder, antisocial personality disorder, psychopathy, and DSPD all denote rather different but overlapping groups. The following diagram (Figure 2.1) illustrates the connection between the definitions of antisocial behaviour in adolescence and the development of personality disorders in adulthood. The hourglass represents the transition from adolescence (in the top of the hourglass) to adulthood (in the lower half of the hourglass). About a third of the general population of adolescents behave in an antisocial way, to the extent that they break the law (although not always being caught). The behaviour of most of this category is limited to adolescence, but for a small sub-set the behaviour will have been manifest in earlier childhood and will persist into adulthood, and may develop into a personality disorder. One type of personality disorder is ASPD and a tiny sub-set of this sub category will present as dangerous (the tip of the population in the lower section of the hourglass).

By focusing on ASPD, in this report we are excluding the majority of people who commit at least some antisocial behaviours in their lifetime, and we are drawing on a slightly larger group than those who are likely to be described as DSPD. The category of individuals we are concerned with will, therefore, have met diagnostic criteria for ASPD at some point in their lives, will have committed illegal acts, and may go on to be dangerous at a later point.

Figure 2.1 **Schematic representation of diagnostic categories and estimated prevalence of types of adolescent antisocial behaviour and adult personality disorders**

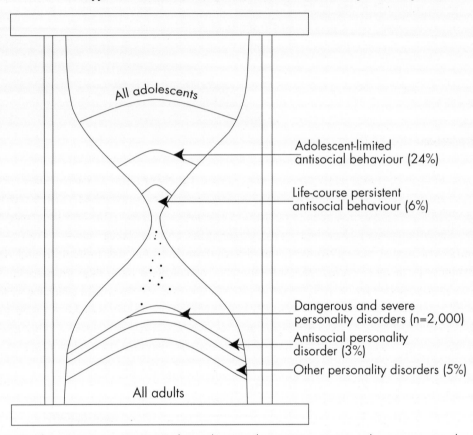

N.B. These estimates may vary depending on diagnostic criteria and assessment tools, and are based on recently reported rates (e.g. Moffitt et al, 1996; Robins and Regier, 1991; Home Office, 1999.)

The remainder of this report highlights what is and what is not known about preventing ASPD. This requires reference to the literature on all the groups mentioned in this chapter, since prevention and intervention for antisocial behaviour in adolescence is directly relevant to prevention of ASPD. As we have seen, some antisocial adolescents will present as ASPD in adulthood, but most will not.

Moreover, these groups are dynamic rather than static; people move in and out of different diagnoses throughout their life-course. The challenge is predicting who will fall into which group on the basis of limited childhood data, and then assessing whether any of those who did not turn out to be ASPD were in fact successfully treated in some way.

3

The main risk factors: foci for prevention and intervention

Introduction

Any intervention, preventative or otherwise, should be informed by evidence-based, life-course models of development. Understanding the causal processes involved in the evolution of personality disorders is essential for effective prevention. However, causal factors need to be distinguished from factors that are antecedent but are not directly causal. There is a need, as Rutter et al (1998) state, 'to differentiate between risk indicators and risk mechanisms'. In other words, research needs to demonstrate more than an association between a particular factor and an outcome. It needs to uncover the way in which the factor of interest operates to produce its effect. For example, family discord may be a risk factor, but the risk mechanism may involve physical abuse towards a child, producing disturbed attachment patterns and aggressive interpersonal style, leading to antisocial behaviour.

With greater understanding of risk mechanisms, we may begin to intervene in the development of disorder by targeting key factors at a critical stage in a child's life. However, where personality disorders are concerned, Coid (1999) comments that aetiology has been neglected, and stresses the need to uncover whether the constitutional and/or environmental factors implicated are, for example, additive until they reach a certain threshold, require a sufficient level of severity, or must occur at a critical developmental phase during the lifespan.

Offord and Reitsma-Street (1983) raise similar concerns in relation to the aetiology of antisocial behaviour. Specifically, they suggest that additive factors (where the effect of the factors is equal to the sum of each of their effects in isolation) need to be delineated from those that are transactional (where one factor increases the likelihood of experiencing another) or interactive (where the two factors potentiate each other and produce an overall effect greater than the sum of the individual effects). Concepts such as cumulative disadvantages (Sampson & Laub, 1993) and interactional and cumulative continuities (Caspi & Moffitt, 1995) have been devised to describe the linkages of factors involved. An illustration of an interactional continuity, for example, is the relationship between childhood economic disadvantage and the development of antisocial behaviours, in which adverse parenting practices have been found to play a mediating role (Larzelere & Patterson, 1990). Untangling such mechanisms is crucial to identifying the factors interventions need to address, and the life stage at which they need to be tackled.

Another important distinction to be made between the various risk factors for any disorder are those which are fixed risk factors and those which are *variable risk factors* (Kraemer et al, 1997). The former are a group of 'static' factors (Audit Commission, 1996) involving features such as gender, age and genetic inheritance, which cannot be changed but are useful in defining groups who should be targeted for preventative intervention. Variable factors by contrast are 'dynamic' factors that can potentially be modified to alter risk, and include social skills and cognitive biases.

Methodological considerations

It is clear that longitudinal studies are important for identifying risk factors and mechanisms. A number of such studies have been conducted both in the UK and abroad, and these have contributed considerably to understanding of the development of antisocial behaviour. They have several advantages over cross-sectional studies. They are able, for example, to clarify the chains of effects between potential causal factors, to identify critical periods in development, and to identify different developmental pathways that may lead to the same outcome. They permit the study of onset, persistence, escalation and desistance so that the effects of any given factor at different stages in a child's development may be established. They are, therefore, fundamental to the design of interventions, early or late.

In addition to longitudinal research, experimental studies in which interactive variables for specific risk groups can be modified are useful for suggesting causality. Loeber and Farrington (1997) suggest using a combination of both types of design in the study of antisocial behaviour. Further details of other methodological recommendations for studies of risk factors can also be found in Farrington (1999) and Offord and Reitsma-Street (1983).

Risk factors

There are relatively few studies of potential causal processes in the development of personality disorders, although there are several comprehensive reviews and commentaries on risk factors for ASPD and more common outcomes such as antisocial behaviour (e.g. Dolan & Coid, 1993; Farrington, 1999; Lahey, Waldman, & McBurnett, 1999; Rutter et al, 1998; Yoshikawa, 1994). For the purpose of the present review, a limited range of risk factors has been selected for discussion. The factors selected are those of greatest significance for identifying target groups and for the design of interventions themselves, and predominantly concern biology, individual and family functioning.

Genetic influences

Evidence suggests that genetic factors play a modest to moderate role in the development of early-onset antisocial behaviour. Adolescent-limited disorder is thought to be far less genetically determined than life-course persistent disorder (Lahey et al, 1999). A number of studies have found an association between ASPD in adults and behavioural problems in their children (e.g. Stewart & Leone, 1978), leading Kendler, Davis and Kessler (1997) to suggest genetic links. Others place more emphasis on the interplay of genetic and environmental influences (e.g. Caprara & Rutter, 1995; Lahey et al, 1999; Rutter, 1997). It is possible that genetic influences have an indirect impact on the development of antisocial behaviour, and operate by influencing temperamental predispositions, particularly oppositional temperament, which in turn influence adverse social interactions that lead to antisocial behaviour.

Findings from adoptee studies, case-control investigations and longitudinal studies also suggest that biological vulnerabilities require environmental interaction. In a study involving 197 adoptees, adverse adoptive home environment was associated with an increased rate of aggression and conduct problems in adoptees, but only for those with a biological background of ASPD (Cadoret et al, 1995). Studies examining the effects of parental loss or separation also suggest a role for genetic influence in conjunction with environmental influences. One study, for example, found that among clinic-referred boys whose parents were divorced, more than twice as many boys with a parent with ASPD received a diagnosis of conduct disorder than boys without a parent with ASPD. No significant association was found between divorce and conduct disorder in the absence of parental ASPD (Lahey et al, 1988). Quinton and Rutter (1988) also reported that persistent conduct problems were greatest amongst children who were exposed to both hostile parenting and parents with a personality disorder. In terms of identifying children and young people for interventions, having a parent with ASPD is likely to be a significant factor in raising risk of ASPD in the child, whether effects are mediated genetically or environmentally.

Temperament

Differences in temperament that are apparent in pre-school years may have implications for the later development of antisocial behaviour. Caspi and others (1995) found that 'lack of control' at the age of three years (combining emotional liability, restlessness, short attention span, and negativism) in the Dunedin sample predicted disruptive and antisocial behaviour at ages 9-15 years. Tremblay and others (1994) found that impulsivity assessed in terms of fidgetiness and over-activity was the best predictor of delinquency at the age of 13 years.

A review of studies of aggression by Parker and Asher (1987) reported that early aggression was a predictor of later delinquency. Coie and others (1995) have found that the best predictor of later antisocial behaviour was a combination of early aggression and peer rejection. Various forms of aggression have been delineated in order to find the form most likely to persist. For example, offensive (unprovoked) aggression has been distinguished from defensive (provoked) aggression, with only the latter being associated with later criminality (Pulkkinen, 1987). In terms of interventions, identification of impulsivity, lack of control, and aggression in young children may form a marker of later antisocial behaviour.

Childhood antisocial behaviour

An area of investigation that has implications for identifying who should be targeted for interventions concerns antisocial behaviour in childhood. Life-course persistent antisocial behaviour has been distinguished from adolescent-limited antisocial behaviour (Moffitt, 1993), as described in Chapter 2. (These two forms of conduct disorder are also delineated in DSM-IV, based on onset of symptoms before or after the age of 10, although the reliability of estimates of age of onset has recently been called into question – see Sanford et al, 1999.) Life-course persistent antisocial behaviour is more likely to be chronic and severe, and is characterised by physical aggression and violence, the presence of learning difficulties and family pathology, and a cold, callous, alienated, and suspicious interpersonal style (Moffitt et al, 1996). In contrast, adolescent-limited antisocial behaviour is primarily characterised by deviant peer group association, and a rebellious personality style that rejects traditional status hierarchies.

Extension of this basic two-pathway model of conduct disorder has led to the suggestion that within the life-course persistent group there may be a sub-group with a worse prognosis, characterised by inattentive, impulsive and hyperactive behaviours, as seen in attention-deficit/hyperactivity disorder (ADHD) (Lynam, 1996). A longitudinal study of hyperactive children followed up for 15 years, for example, found that 23 per cent had a diagnosis of

ASPD in adulthood compared with two per cent of matched control subjects (Weiss et al, 1985). A similar longitudinal study using more stringent criteria for ASPD reported rates of 12 per cent amongst hyperactive children grown up compared with three per cent amongst controls (Mannuzza et al, 1998). Lynam (1996) reviews further studies highlighting the significance of conduct disorder with ADHD for the development of ASPD.

A sub-group of life-course persistent antisocial children can also be distinguished on the basis of a cold and callous interpersonal style, manipulativeness, a lack of empathy, a lack of guilt, and emotional constrictedness, similar to the personality features that characterise adult psychopaths. In comparison to other children with life-course persistent antisocial behaviour, the callous, unemotional group exhibit greater numbers of conduct problems, more varied conduct problems, have more contact with the police, have a stronger family history of parental ASPD, and are reported to have a *higher IQ* (Christian et al, 1997). Rather than constituting risk factors per se, such cold and callous traits may represent prodromal signs of emerging ASPD. Although long-term data are not available to assess the relationship between this sub-group and ASPD in adulthood, they may represent a group who should be targeted for future intervention.

It has been suggested that the developmental pathways associated with these variants of antisocial behaviour may be quite distinct. Understanding these pathways may help to target the factors of significance for interventions. As yet, however, we do not have sufficient knowledge of aetiology to pinpoint which of the causal pathways in child-onset conduct disorder is of significance for the development of ASPD and other severe personality disorders in adulthood (Silverthorn & Frick, 1999).

Gender

Differences in rates of antisocial behaviour according to gender have been demonstrated in several studies (Offord, Alder & Boyle, 1986; Robins, 1986), although this difference varies according to the age at which it is measured. Generally, in adolescence, conduct problems increase for boys and girls, but the ratio of male to female conduct problems remains high at about 4:1 (Cohen et al, 1993). Whether such differences are due to biological or social causes is debatable, and factors such as sex role socialisation, sex hormone level, and differential rates of physical development have all been implicated.

Recent research suggests that the two-pathway model of early versus adolescent-onset antisocial behaviour described above is more applicable to males than females. For females, there appears to be a group for whom antisocial behaviour arises in adolescence rather than childhood, and, unlike males, persists into adulthood. This has been called the 'delayed onset' pathway (Silverthorn & Frick, 1999). In addition, there is evidence for an *adult-onset* group, which forms the largest sub-group of antisocial behaviour amongst women, estimated to affect 3.5 per cent of the female population (Kratzer & Hodgins, 1996). Overall relatively little is known about them, although they are less likely to be recidivist (Hamalainen & Pulkkinen, 1995).

Given these gender differences in developmental pathways, the optimal timing for identifying and intervening in order to target those with poor long-term prognosis may vary by gender. However, antisocial behaviour and its relation to ASPD in adulthood for females is a relatively under-studied area, and there is still much that needs to be researched before we can begin to identify the very small number of girls who develop ASPD in adulthood.

Co-morbid conditions

The presence of co-occurring conditions such as substance abuse, anxiety, depression, self-harm and suicide attempts may hinder the treatment of antisocial behaviour, and suggests a poorer long-term prognosis (Capaldi & Stoolmiller, 1999; Randall et al, 1999). A recent longitudinal study of 551 community-based youths, for example, has shown that the presence of internalising disorders such as anxiety and depression in addition to externalising disorders such as conduct disorder increased the risk of having a personality disorder in adulthood (Kasen et al, 1999). Where interventions are concerned, Kasen and colleagues (op cit) suggest that affective disorders in children and adolescents need to be diagnosed and treated in addition to their antisocial behaviour, given that DSM-IV Axis I disorders in children may be more amenable to intervention than personality disorders in adulthood.

Biased cognitive processing

A number of studies by Dodge and colleagues have shed light on biases in social information processing in aggressive individuals. They suggest that such individuals have a tendency to selectively focus on aggressive cues rather than non-aggressive ones, and to wrongly attribute hostile intent to neutral or ambiguous social situations (Dodge, 1980, 1986; Dodge & Schwartz, 1997). Furthermore, hostile attributional biases have predicted aggressive behaviour, although only to a moderate degree. Research also shows that aggressive children hold positive attitudes towards aggression, and particularly with proactive aggression such as bullying (Dodge & Schwartz, 1997).

Dodge and colleagues suggest that social information processing partially mediates the effects of early child abuse in predisposing to later conduct problems (Dodge et al, 1995), and that individuals who have been the victim of negative behaviour may readily attribute hostile intent to others. In terms of implication for interventions, these results suggest that a potential area to tackle in antisocial young people in specific contexts is the way in which they read social situations and carry out social problem solving.

Parenting practices

There is evidence to suggest that several aspects of parenting influence children's risk for antisocial behaviour. The parenting practices implicated include neglect, lax supervision, harsh or erratic discipline, and physical and sexual abuse (though the latter may involve a non-familial perpetrator). Coid (1999) found that 'severe examples of adverse early environment, primarily experienced within family of origin' were associated with ASPD in adulthood amongst detainees in maximum-security hospitals and prisons. This finding is also echoed by a number of cross-sectional studies using other types of samples (e.g. Frick, Christian and Wooton, 1999) although the direction of causality between parenting and antisocial behaviour cannot be assumed. However, results from longitudinal studies (in which causal direction is less ambiguous) also provide evidence of a link with offending and delinquency (Farrington and West, 1990). In terms of antisocial personality disorder as a specific outcome, results from US longitudinal studies show that individuals who have experienced neglect and/ or abuse in childhood are up to four times more likely to be diagnosed with a personality disorder in adulthood compared to non-abused others (Johnson et al, 1999; Luntz & Widom, 1994). However, recent research suggests that there may be a sub-group of cold, callous children who display a high rate of conduct problems regardless of the quality of parenting they experience (Wootton et al, 1997).

In addition to parenting practices, other family-related risk factors implicated in the development of antisocial behaviour include family conflict and aggression, discord between parents, and witnessing violence (see Howell et al, 1995; Rutter et al, 1998 for a review). However, higher rates of both internalising and externalising disorder are found in families characterised by hostility between parents, suggesting that this is a relatively non-specific risk factor (Yoshikawa, 1994). The mechanisms involved in these associations are still unclear, although it has been suggested that the effects of marital conflict on adolescent externalising behaviour may be mediated by parental rejection-withdrawal (Fauber et al, 1990).

In terms of interventions, the above results imply that tackling child-parent interaction as well as altering the way in which parents manage their children may assist in the reduction of antisocial behaviour. However, whether interventions based on parenting practices can impact on the very severe antisocial behaviour that usually precedes ASPD in adulthood remains doubtful, especially given the findings discussed above that suggest parenting practices make little difference to children with psychopathic traits (Wootton et al, 1997). These issues are discussed further in Chapter 6, which discusses interventions with adolescents.

Summary of risk factors

To illustrate the breadth of potential risk factors involved in ASPD, a list of risk factors and illustrative studies of risk have been compiled in Table 3.1, with a brief description of their relevance for intervention. As can be seen from Table 3.1, many of the risk factors have been implicated in the pathogenesis of a variety of Axis I and II disorders. Indeed, many of the risk factors have also been implicated in the aetiology of general criminal behaviour, and further studies are required to increase knowledge of risks specific to ASPD.

Table 3.1: Overview of risk factors for antisocial personality disorder

Type of risk factor and illustrative study and implication for intervention

Physiological/ Biological risk factors

Physiological differences e.g. frontal lobe dysfunction (Deckel et al, 1996) lower 5-HT function (Tuinier et al, 1995) increased testosterone (Olweus et al, 1980)	Biological differences believed to influence behavioural inhibition, impulsivity, and aggression. Cross-sectional studies in which direction of causality is unclear, as biological functioning may be altered by experiences and vice versa. May have implications for drug treatment.
Obstetric complications Lewis et al, 1979; Raine et al, 1994	Brain damage assumed as result of obstetric complications, but not directly assessed. Evidence inconclusive as effects may be due to related psychosocial risk factors. Implications for intervention minimal based on current evidence.

Mineral toxicity and dietary risks
e.g. *alcohol in pregnancy (Rutter, 1989)*
lead (Needleman et al, 1996) food
intolerance (Taylor, 1991)

Some evidence for link between alcohol in pregnancy and later hyperactivity and inattention. Dietary advice for pregnant women may reduce risks. Significance of lead and dietary elements relative to other psychosocial risks is not known, and is likely to affect only a small number of children.

Genetic inheritance
Silberg et al, 1996a,b;
DiLalla & Gottesman, 1989

Genetic influence strongest in cases of antisocial behaviour associated with hyperactivity, and also with life-course persistent antisocial behaviour. May have relevance for identifying target group for intervention.

Individual risk factors

Temperament
e.g. *impulsivity (Tremblay et al, 1994)*
lack of control (Caspi et al, 1995)
aggression (Coie et al, 1995)

Temperamental characteristics assessed in pre-school children predict delinquency, externalising disorder and antisocial behaviour in teenage years and early adulthood. May be a factor for identifying young children for early interventions.

Childhood antisocial behaviour
e.g. *conduct disorder (Moffitt et al, 1996)*
ADHD (Lynam, 1996)

Early-onset conduct disorder, especially when co-morbid with ADHD, has a very poor prognosis and is predictive of ASPD. These factors may assist in identifying target group for intervention. Early treatment of ADHD may reduce risk.

Gender
Kratzer & Hodgins, 1996

Conduct disorder more common in males. May be due to biological differences or differences in socialisation. May involve different gender-specific causal pathways, which have implications for timing and nature of intervention.

Co-morbid disorders

e.g. *depression, anxiety (Kasen et al,
1999)
substance abuse (Randall et al,
1999)*

Individuals with conditions co-morbid with conduct problems have worse prognosis in terms of severity and duration of antisocial behaviour later in life. Treatment of one disorder may improve long-term outcome with the other.

Biased cognitive processing

e.g. *attributing hostile intent
(Dodge & Schwartz, 1997)*

Aggressive individuals attribute hostile intent inappropriately and more readily, and focus on aggressive social cues. May be a mediating factor between early childhood abuse and later conduct problems. Implications for social problem-solving and social skills training in aggressive individuals.

Educational factors

e.g low IQ (Hirschi & Hindelang, 1977; Maguin & Loeber, 1996)
reading difficulties (Maughan et al, 1996)

Antisocial behaviour is associated with lower IQ and poor language development in pre-school years. Possible mechanism for links via impaired social problem-solving skills, reading difficulties and low education attainment. Evidence for link via hyperactivity and inattention. Further studies needed to investigate mechanism, and implications for intervention.

Family risk factors

Family structure

e.g. *loss/separation (Lahey et al, 1988)
adoption (Sullivan et al, 1995)*

Evidence suggests that family processes rather than loss, separation or adoption experiences per se are of more significance for prediction of antisocial behaviour.

Parenting practices
e.g. harsh discipline, lax supervision
(Farrington & West, 1990;
Wootton et al, 1997)
neglect and abuse (Luntz &
Widom,

Family conflict and violence
Fauber et al, 1990

Parental psychiatric conditions
e.g. parental ASPD (Cadoret et al,
1995)
parental alcoholism (Rutter, 1989)

Parenting practices and child maltreatment associated with later antisocial behaviour. Mechanism involved is not known. Parent training programmes may alter risk, but are unlikely to impact on severe, persistent antisocial behaviour.

Marital conflict may increase antisocial behaviour in child via effects on parenting practices.

Influence of parental psychiatric status on child's antisocial behaviour may be mediated via genetic link or by environmentally determined processes such as parenting practices. Parents with ASPD may be a useful target group for early intervention with their children.

Peer group risk factors

Deviant peers
Sampson & Laub, 1993

Antisocial behaviour more common in individuals with deviant peer groups. Peer group influences more likely in adolescent-limited rather than life-course persistent antisocial behaviour. Withdrawal from antisocial peers (as a single intervention) has not been found to reduce offending.

Peer rejection
Coie et al, 1995

Social rejection associated with incompetent social functioning is predictive of poor outcome. This finding is more applicable to early-onset antisocial behaviour. Suggests a role for early social skills training.

Community risk factors

Poverty, socio-economic status
Conger et al, 1995

Risk from social disadvantage mainly mediated by stresses on family functioning. Tackling more proximal risk factors may be more beneficial to those of highest risk.

Unemployment
Farrington et al, 1986

Unemployment raises risk of criminal activities in individuals already at high risk. Need to know more about the mechanisms involved before preventative measures can be developed.

Protective factors

Even when individuals have been exposed to adverse circumstances that are likely to influence their later psychopathology, some individuals will not succumb to disorder. These individuals may be resilient to the effects of adversity due to the presence of certain protective factors. The nature of such factors can vary, and may involve dispositional attributes, environmental conditions, or events that mitigate against negative experiences (Garmezy, 1981). Protective factors may operate in several ways, which have been described in detail by other authors (e.g. Rutter et al, 1998) and include, for example, reducing sensitivity to risk, reducing the impact of the risk, reducing negative chain reactions, and increasing positive chain reactions.

Very little is known about protective factors in the development of ASPD. Some studies have examined factors protecting against outcomes such as delinquency in adolescence, and antisocial behaviour in young adulthood (West & Farrington, 1977). Of the few studies that report on such outcomes, the protective factors identified have tended to focus on close relationships with key individuals. Farrington and West (1995), for example, found that delinquency was a less likely outcome for young males who formed a stable relationship with a girlfriend or wife. Similarly, in a study of childhood victims of sexual abuse, Skuse and colleagues at Great Ormond Street Hospital found that abused young men were less likely to become perpetrators of sexual abuse if they managed to form a close relationship with a key figure, whether this was a peer, sibling or adult (Skuse et al, 1999). In terms of ASPD as an outcome, much more investigation is required before we can use our knowledge of protective factors to inform the design of interventions.

Conclusions

Most children and young people with the risk factors described above will not develop conditions as rare or severe as ASPD in adulthood. However, knowledge of the risk factors discussed above may narrow down the selection of individuals who are at highest risk for the development of ASPD, and give some clues as to the areas that interventions should tackle. The target group are likely to be boys who have early-onset conduct disorder co-morbid with ADHD, with difficult temperaments in pre-school years, who in adolescence are likely to be suicidal and self-harming, and misuse drugs/alcohol or experience depression. They are likely to have experienced extreme neglect, abuse, or harsh discipline from caregivers who themselves may have severe psychiatric problems.

We remain much more in the dark concerning the developmental pathways for ASPD in girls. Even amongst a group with this combination of risk factors, only a minority will develop ASPD. Our knowledge of risk factors for this rare condition is still very underdeveloped, with the result that any current attempts to identify a target population will result in a large 'false positive' group. Furthermore, little is known about the specificity of risks for ASPD, since many of the risk factors implicated in the disorder are also linked to other disorders.

Adolescents at risk for ASPD are likely to have been exposed to multiple risk factors across their life course, and are also likely to experience many problems in functioning. It is therefore unlikely that tackling any one risk factor alone will sufficiently impact on a group with complex problems and needs. Interventions that are able to address multiple causes are likely to be required at multiple points across the life course. The issue is discussed fully in Chapter 6, which concerns specific examples of interventions.

Rutter (1997) pinpoints five key questions that remain unresolved in relation to risk factors for antisocial behaviour. These concern who should be targeted for intervention and what factors in their genetic or psychosocial make-up should be tackled. First, few studies are able to distinguish between environmental and genetic mediation. It is known, for example, that a parent's antisocial behaviour is a predictor of antisocial behaviour in their offspring, but it is still unclear to what extent this effect is genetically or environmentally determined. Second, little is known about the mode of operation of a risk factor such as, for example, family discord. We need to explore how far discord must be focused on a child in order to increase risk, and whether marital conflict operates in the same way. Third, little is known about the way in which environmental risk factors affect individuals, and have the power to influence outcomes many years after their initial impact. The process may involve changes in social information processing (Dodge et al, 1995), disturbances in attachment patterns (Greenberg, Speltz, &DeKlyen, 1993), alterations in patterns of learned behaviour (Patterson, 1995), or even reorganisation of neurons (Goodman, 1994), depending on the theoretical perspective adopted. Fourth, the means by which broad social factors such as schools, peer groups, community and poverty influence risk requires further exploration. It is possible that some of these factors have an effect through their adverse influence on more proximal factors such as parenting and family relationships (e.g. Patterson, 1995). Finally, Rutter suggests that we still lack understanding of the extent to which environmental effects are restricted to children who are genetically at risk. There are clearly many gaps in our knowledge of ASPD that have yet to filled, and are likely to limit the effectiveness of any initiative aimed at prevention.

4   Designing and evaluating interventions for high-risk adolescents

Introduction

Before looking at the results of existing programmes, two tasks remain. The first is to consider, at a general level, the main design issues both of interventions and also of evaluations of interventions. The second is to consider how high-risk young people might be selected to take part in interventions. If significant research design faults are pervasive in the literature, and if we cannot be precise about which particular young people are most at risk, the basis of our knowledge about which interventions actually work is seriously jeopardised. We begin the present chapter therefore with a discussion of the design of interventions, including the timing of interventions. We then move on to discuss the design of studies to evaluate interventions.

Design of interventions

How to intervene

When considering how to intervene, thought must be given to the age group at which the intervention is targeted, the stage in the development of the disorder, and the size of the target population. *Primary intervention* strategies involve early prevention of the occurrence of the disorder, for example, by intervening with high-risk parents following the birth of a child or at the pre-school age. *Secondary intervention* involves intervention at the first or prodromal signs of the disorder, for example, with a child who displays attention problems or impulsiveness. When a disorder has already developed, *tertiary intervention* may be implemented to limit the impact of the disorder or to ensure rehabilitation.

The intervention itself may vary in terms of the proportion of the population it targets. *Universal programmes* are usually aimed at the whole population in a community, on the basis of a common risk factor such as poverty. Such interventions are less likely to label children than other interventions (Kellam & Rebok, 1992). They usually cost less per child but are not necessarily economical given the large numbers of children involved unless the intervention is of proven efficacy. *Selected programmes*, in contrast, are directed at sub-groups of the population who are at high risk for disorders, for example, children who are experiencing abuse, or have deficits in social skills. Finally, *indicated programmes* focus on individuals who already show signs of disorder.

As we saw in the discussion of risk factors, it is clear that young people who are at risk for personality disorders are already difficult to manage as children.However, we also concluded that the risk factors are not specific to ASPD, but apply to a range of disorders.To what extent is it sensible or possible to target interventions at the very early stages of the development of this rare disorder? On the one hand, there is a need to consider the wisdom of leaving an intervention until adolescence when in fact risk factors for the disorder may arise earlier in childhood.On the other hand, our ability to predict which children will grow up to have what type of disorder is very poor, diminishing our ability to target development of any one type of problem.In the next section we go on to discuss the merits of early versus late interventions for ASPD.

When to intervene: early versus late interventions

Interventions may be described as 'early' either on the basis that they are targeted at younger children or else in terms of the stage in the development of the disorder which they tackle (Little & Mount, 1999). Where a disorder is known to persist into adulthood, for example, intervention in teenage years may be described as 'early' even though the intervention may occur at a relatively late stage of childhood.

Advocates of early intervention are generally of the opinion that it is easier to influence individuals prior to the onset of symptoms than it is to influence outcome once antisocial behaviour has become a habitual pattern. There may be great benefits to be gained by primary intervention in some instances, especially where an intervention targets a factor known to be associated with multiple adverse outcomes. For example, poor parenting practices are associated with several negative outcomes in offspring, including delinquency (Larzelere & Patterson, 1990), substance dependency (Chilcoat & Anthony, 1996) and depression in adulthood (Bifulco & Moran, 1998). Hence intervention aimed at improving parenting skills might expect to produce improvements in a number of areas. In addition, if risk is cumulative, then early intervention may reduce exposure to later risks and ultimately alter long-term trajectory for the better.

Currently in the UK, a number of government initiatives are underway which address problems in several areas that influence early child development, including parenting, education, substance misuse, offending, and provision of mental health services for children (e.g. Sure Start; National Literacy Strategy; On-Track; Quality Protects). The government is also aiming to improve child and mental health services by increasing staff levels, providing greater staff training, and supporting multi-agency working. Substance misuse has also been identified as an important area to be tackled in relation to children and young people, and additional funding is to be spent in order to assist those at risk. Given that substance misuse often accompanies severe antisocial behaviour, there is an argument that this initiative may help to reduce the severity or incidence of ASPD.

Where personality disorders are concerned, in theory it may be possible to use interventions with children who are pre-school age, given that, as we discussed in Chapter 3, temperamental differences and problems such as ADHD displayed as early as the age of three years have been shown to be predictive of poorer prognosis. However, we concluded that the particular constellation of early childhood factors predicting severe antisocial outcomes is not yet known. In addition, even if knowledge of risk factors was sufficiently advanced to be able to identify a young sample for intervention, the ability to identify a problem early may not necessarily be paralleled by our ability to develop a means of dealing with it at that stage (Little & Mount, 1999), and the nature of the intervention itself therefore may still be ill-defined.

It is too early to judge the impact of the current range of early preventative initiatives underway in the UK, although evidence from the US and elsewhere has shown some promising results with generally disadvantaged children when similar programmes have been introduced (e.g. Olweus, 1993). It seems likely that the current initiatives will have positive effects on a range of risk factors associated with child and adolescent mental health problems. However, it is important to note that many early intervention programmes with pre-adolescents have been found to be least effective with individuals whose antisocial behaviour is severe and more chronic, and also for individuals with co-morbid conditions (e.g. Kazdin, 1995). Such individuals are, of course, the group most likely to develop personality disorders in adulthood. This is confirmed by results from a number of universal and selected preventative measures aimed at the level of peer, school and community intervention (many of which are reviewed by Brewer et al, 1995). They include peer counselling, mentoring, gang prevention, school initiatives such as Positive Action Through Holistic Education (PATHE), and community-wide interventions such as 'Communities That Care'. Results from evaluations of such interventions show that they have limited success with adolescents, and may only succeed in altering outcomes for those individuals with relatively mild antisocial behaviour.

In contrast to those who believe that 'prevention is better than cure' are those who believe in the efficacy of secondary or even tertiary intervention, and support the 'risk principle' put forward by Andrews and others (1996). The risk principle upholds the notion that intervention is most effective when the individual being treated has appreciable risk of an adverse outcome. In other words, there must be potential for antisocial behaviour before antisocial behaviour can be inhibited. If predictive accuracy and minimising false positives are seen as important features of an intervention, perhaps on the grounds of cost-effectiveness, then later rather than early intervention may be preferable. The further down the various pathways to social and psychological problems the child goes, the more predictable his or her behaviour becomes. For example, results from the Cambridge study of working class boys showed that a third of the eight year olds followed up had been convicted by the time they were 25, but as many as 60 per cent of those convicted in adolescence were convicted again in adulthood (Farrington, 1995).

Hence, for a disorder that has a particularly low base rate such as ASPD, accurate identification of individuals at risk may only be possible after repeated court appearances, since an early sustained criminal career is a precursor of adult personality disorder. However, targeting intervention at high-risk adolescents rather than younger children means that a number of serious offences may already have been committed, some of which might have been prevented with earlier intervention. Also, contact with various services may already have occurred, leading to use of costly resources. In addition, it needs to be borne in mind that antisocial behaviour that has become habitual may prove resistant to treatment or difficult to engage (Farrington, 1995). Where individuals with the potential to develop personality disorders are concerned, engagement in treatment is likely to be a problematic issue. However, this should not form a barrier to offering interventions to particularly high-risk groups, but suggests that innovative methods of delivering the interventions are required.

Multiple gates: a mixed model for intervention

Given what is known about the diverse range of problems and level of poor adjustment and functioning in high-risk adolescents, it seems unlikely that any single intervention, even if delivered early in life, is likely to be sufficient to prevent personality disorder in later life. Therefore multiple interventions are more likely to succeed, and may need to be delivered at several points in the life course, including interventions with adolescents. Little and Mount (1999) similarly argue that an approach involving different sorts of interventions taking place at several stages of a child's development is more likely to achieve success. This seems a suitable strategy where the development of personality disorders is concerned given the multiple areas of difficulties and deficits seen in such individuals.

Rather than making a choice between the use of either early or late intervention, the principle of 'multiple gates' may thus represent a useful way forward in prevention of ASPD in adulthood. Successive interventions could be applied, moving from the universal to the selected, and indicated measures, in line with the severity of a child's behaviour as it emerges over time. Thus children who have not benefited from a universal prevention programme and who continue to display difficulties may be further referred to a secondary intervention programme. Alternatively, special components could be added to a primary prevention programme for children perceived to be at highest risk. Several authors have suggested that a system of multiple gates may be useful in the prevention of juvenile delinquency (Kellam & Rebok, 1992; Le Blanc, 1998). This model has not been tested where prevention of personality disorders in adulthood is concerned. Given the complex web of factors leading to personality disorder in adulthood, as well as the possibility that different risk factors become salient at different points in the developmental pathway, the use of multiple gates may be preferable. However, what remains untested is the optimal number of gates and the ages at which they should be applied.

Developmental models

Ideally, in addition to knowledge of risk and protective factors, the question of when to intervene to offset development of ASPD should also be guided by knowledge of the developmental processes involved in character formation. 'Character' has been defined as 'an individual's general responsiveness to the dilemma and responsibilities of social life' (Hay et al, 1994). If we can understand 'normal' developmental processes and the impact that risk factors have on them, then we may gain insight into the optimal time to intervene. We may be able to steer children towards positive character development (involving empathy and co-operativeness) and away from antisocial characteristics (such as cruelty and callousness). This requires understanding of the acquisition of a number of features such as 'prosocial behaviour and altruism, self-regulation and self-control, acquisition of social conventions and moral values, honesty and integrity' (Hay et al, 1994).

Many of these aspects of character begin to develop during pre-school years, and continue to do so across the entire life span. Adolescence in particular is a key time for the development of moral reasoning. In Piaget's theory of cognitive development, there are a number of stages in cognitive development, each stage involving more sophisticated reasoning than the previous one (Piaget, 1972). According to this theory, the final stage of cognitive development typically emerges in adolescence. This is the stage of 'formal operations' which allows adolescents to think beyond the present and to analytically reflect on their own thinking, in the same way that adults do. The development of such abstract reasoning during adolescence paves the way for the ability to reason ethically and for the development of 'moral autonomy'.

Kohlberg's (1964) theory of moral development is also based on the notion of stages that must be transgressed, involving the self in relation to society's conventions. Individuals shift from viewing rules as external to, and imposed upon, the self, to seeing society's rules from the social perspective of a member of society, involving the ability to understand and identify with them. Finally, in adolescence, the individual develops the ability to define moral values as principles voluntarily taken, rather than conventional standards to be upheld. A review of evidence concerning Kohlberg's theory suggests that it is less universal than first thought. Moral reasoning may vary, for example, by gender and culture (Muuss, 1996). Evidence also suggests that individuals may regress to less mature moral reasoning stages, and that different moral stages may be used in different situations, i.e. moral reasoning may be domain specific rather than structural.

Appreciation of a young person's cognitive ability (including moral development) may be critical at several stages of the judicial processes, influencing, for example, the age of criminal responsibility, the type of intervention offered as well as the way it is delivered. Interventions therefore need to be sensitive to the level of cognitive and moral development of a young person with antisocial behaviour. Exposure to higher levels of moral reasoning may stimulate development of moral maturity (Power, Higgins, & Kohlberg, 1989). Interventions tackling aspects of character formation involving moral reasoning training may provide young people with the ability to reason in ways that are more morally mature, and therefore potentially less antisocial. However, acquisition of the ability to identify morally correct behaviour does not necessarily lead a person to act in a morally responsible way, although there is evidence for a link between the two (Trevethan & Walker, 1989).

A recent study reports that adolescents view engaging in risky activities (such as delinquent behaviour and substance misuse) as a personal decision, outside of the domains of societal regulation or moral concern (Kuther & Higgins-D'Alessandro, 2000). Personal issues concern non-social acts involving the individual's safety, harm to self, comfort and health. Whilst risky activities may harm the individual, adolescents may still feel they derive benefit from them because of gains in friendship formation, identity formation, and so on. On the basis of these findings, Kuther and Higgins-D'Alesandro (2000) make a number of suggestions concerning interventions aimed at reducing risky and antisocial activities in adolescence. First, they highlight the need to recognise the benefits of such behaviours as perceived by adolescents, and to offer alternatives that involve similar benefits but via less dangerous or antisocial activities. Second, they stress the need to shift adolescents' views of risks from being personal choices to those involving morally based decision-making processes, by emphasising the individual's connection with social groups and society. An appreciation of adolescents' moral development may therefore enhance the design of suitable interventions, particularly where interventions for severe antisocial behaviour are concerned. The use of moral reasoning interventions is discussed further in Chapter 6.

Design issues in evaluations of interventions

Once an intervention has been designed and implemented, how can we tell whether or not it worked? Even the best-designed interventions can be the focus of rather poor evaluations, if evaluations exist at all. In this next section we briefly review some of the key problems in determining 'what works'. Many of the studies evaluating interventions contain methodological weaknesses that severely limit the conclusions that can be drawn from them. Negative results can thus reflect flaws in the evaluation rather than the intervention itself (Dolan, 1998). The arguments we summarise in this section are well and frequently rehearsed in the evaluation literature, particularly at this time of explosion of large-scale evaluations of programmes of interventions (e.g. evaluations of Sure Start; On-Track; Youth Justice Board programmes, etc). For more detailed discussions see, for example, Rutter and others (1998).

In a review of treatment studies based on adult psychopaths, Dolan and Coid (1993) set out a number of issues that should be addressed by those conducting studies evaluating treatments or interventions for personality disorders:

- Who is a psychopath and how is the construct measured?
- Is random allocation of subjects to conditions possible or ethical?
- What constitutes treatment and non-treatment?
- What constitutes an acceptable measure of outcome, and how long should the follow-up be?
- What is an adequate sample size to be sure of a statistically significant difference in treatment groups?

The first of these issues raises the need for clear criteria for **defining the target group**, using standardised assessments where possible, whether this is via clinical diagnostic criteria, legislation, or psychosocial measures. The definitions of many disorders remain ill defined in several studies, and terms such as 'dangerous' present the same problem. Where adolescent studies are concerned, groups defined as 'serious violent offenders' or 'delinquents' have often been used, and explicit criteria are required to stipulate precisely the nature of the group. Study populations are sometimes treated as homogeneous when in fact they contain several important sub-groups. For example, they may fail to distinguish between adolescent-limited and early-onset disorder, and those with co-morbid conditions.

The second issue raised by Dolan and Coid (1993) relates to the **random allocation** of subjects to 'treatment' or 'other treatment' or 'no treatment' conditions. This is regarded as the gold standard for the evaluation of interventions, but throws up ethical issues concerning the group who do not receive the intervention. When interventions are short, the control group may subsequently receive treatment. However, treatment for groups with complex needs is likely to be a lengthy process, and delaying potentially successful interventions at what may be a critical time in adolescent development raises serious ethical issues. Random allocation to treatment may pose particular problems in health care settings where there is an onus on the professional to provide treatment. Also, randomisation may not be possible in the context of the judicial system, where courts may demand a particular type of intervention.

Quasi-experimental designs may offer an alternative approach to the use of the randomised control trial. There are several forms of quasi-experimental design. Typically they involve introducing an intervention in one setting but not another, or using natural variations in what occurs as the basis for comparison. In comparative designs, the groups to be contrasted may differ in some way that has the potential to bias results. Therefore, risk characteristics of each group must be carefully assessed to check whether differences in outcomes are a result of initial presentation features (Rutter et al, 1998). The ways in which individuals are selected for treatments must be broadly similar to avoid biases introduced, for example, by differences in levels of co-operation amongst subjects in one condition rather than another.

Another form of quasi-experimental design often used is the single sample pre-post design. This is considerably weaker because it is unclear whether any observed changes in outcome can directly be attributed to the effects of the intervention, or to other factors operating at the same time. If a developmental perspective is assumed, then the baseline for evaluation of the effectiveness of a preventative intervention is not a pre-intervention measure, as in some clinical and drugs trials, but the development trajectory for youngsters of comparable risk status who are not exposed to the intervention (Kellam & Rebok, 1992). However, for a number of reasons it may be impractical to incorporate a comparison group in the study design, which is why many intervention studies use a pre-post treatment approach.

Dolan and Coid's (1993) third point regarding the design of treatment studies concerns **details of the nature of the treatment** or intervention offered. They report that most studies fail to provide an adequate description of the content of the intervention such that replication by another researcher clinician is impossible. Also, details are often lacking of the skills or training or supervision required by staff to carry out the intervention. Similarly, little attention is given to the description of non-treatment in the control group. Those in a 'no treatment' condition may actually receive some sort of intervention during the study period, even if they are community-based and using primary health care or other services, and this needs to be made explicit in descriptions of control samples. Also, when studies involve a multi-modal intervention, it is unclear which of the several elements of the intervention are the most significant for predicting positive outcomes.

What constitutes an appropriate **outcome measure** is also debatable. Recidivism is the most often quoted outcome measure in treatment or intervention studies. However, criminal behaviour may be an inappropriate measure for many disorders, as 'reconviction is not a measure of aggression or irresponsible behaviour, it is a measure of being found guilty or of breaking the law' (p 248; Dolan & Coid, 1993).Recidivism itself may be a source of error in so far as conviction may be influenced by a number of random elements such as having the motivation and opportunity to offend, being identified and apprehended by the police, being charged, and being found guilty (Walker, 1995; Rutter et al, 1998). At the same time, history of previous convictions is predictive of future offending, according to actuarial models.

As an outcome measure, re-hospitalisation rates may also be subject to random influences that invalidate results, as when, for example, an individual may need to be hospitalised but resources are not available. Changes in psychological functioning have sometimes been assessed as the outcome measure, although a wide range has been used, making cross-study comparisons difficult. Also, very few studies have examined the relationship between changes in psychological functioning and personality, and offending behaviour.Where interventions aim to reduce incidence of 'dangerousness', thought needs to be given to how this notion may be operationalised and whether this is different in adolescent versus adult populations. If it involves harm to self and others, then measures or criteria for judging such outcomes need to be devised.

Outcomes the government has expressed concern about include a general reduction in antisocial and offending behaviour, cost-effective use of resources, increased public safety, a reduction in the number of hospital admissions for this group, and improved outcomes for individuals and their families (Home Office/Department of Health, 1999). Cost-effectiveness has been examined to a lesser extent, and is more typically reported in American interventions.

Dolan and Coid (1993) also stress that the durability of changes in behaviour or personality needs to be assessed when designing interventions. This is best accommodated in an intervention study by incorporating a lengthy follow-up if possible, although this will add to the cost of the study. It will be clear from many of the intervention studies reviewed in the chapter to follow that treatment effects are sometimes evident during the weeks or months following discharge, but are absent after two or three years.In a study of young psychopaths at Broadmoor, for example, average length of time from discharge to re-offending was two years (Reiss, Grubin and Meux, 1996). Hence a shorter follow-up would not have provided an accurate picture of re-offending rates.Long-term follow-up with regular, frequent contacts may help to inform us of when 'top-up' interventions or 'booster' sessions are required following initial treatment.

Finally, Dolan and Coid (1993) raise the issue of **statistical power.** They suggest that more homogeneous samples, larger sample sizes, improved accuracy of measurement and use of a lower alpha level (criterion of significance) will all help to improve confidence in the results. However, each of these strategies has drawbacks that may make them impractical to follow. They recommend the use of survival analysis as an appropriate and powerful series of statistical techniques for examining outcome data.

Conclusions

These various methodological shortfalls, both in the design of the original intervention and then in the design of the evaluation, limit the conclusions to be drawn from the literature in an area where there are already precious few studies. Very few interventions have specifically targeted ASPD, and lack of specificity about the early risk factors means that it is very hard to target prevention programmes in early childhood that are intended to prevent the development of this particular disorder. The types of families and children who are most at risk appear to be those most likely to be missed in wide-scale primary prevention programmes. Simply from the point of view of targeting relevant participants, tertiary intervention, or 'indicated programmes' may be more fruitful in terms of impacting on overall numbers with ASPD in adulthood. Alternatively, multiple interventions across the lifespan, involving primary, secondary and tertiary prevention, may be required.

5   Identifying high-risk adolescents

Introduction

How successful can we be at identifying high-risk adolescents as targets for intervention? In this chapter we consider the efficacy of existing methods for determining whether or not young people are showing the early signs of the disorder. We also consider the context in which adolescents with difficult and disturbed behaviour may be located, in terms of existing service provision.

Screening for risk

In selecting individuals for intervention, a balance must be struck between targeting as many 'high-risk' subjects as possible, whilst at the same time excluding subjects of low-risk status. The cost-effectiveness of any intervention will partly depend on the success of this balancing act. With a condition such as ASPD that has a low base rate, the task of identifying those at risk is particularly difficult, especially when there are few guidelines as to what constitute the key risk factors involved.

In studies examining the success of risk assessment, contradictory findings emerge depending on the outcome of interest, the sample being tested, and the context in which the assessment is made. A study assessing predictors of recidivism for serious offences amongst mentally disordered offenders, for example, found that psychopathy was of little significance once previous criminal history had been taken into account (Bonta, Law & Hanson, 1998). However, if violent behaviour is taken as an outcome rather than recidivism, psychopathy has been found to predict outcome over and above factors such as previous criminal history (Hemphill, Hare, & Wong, 1998).

Where future dangerousness is concerned, prediction is a notoriously difficult area, complicated by competing concerns for the rights of the individual versus the importance of protection of the public. Scott (1977) suggests that to be useful, an assessment of dangerousness must specify the behaviour of concern, the potential damage or harm likely to result from the behaviour and also the probability that the behaviour will occur and under what circumstances.

In a recent review of violence risk assessment, Douglas, Cox and Webster (1999) identified several types of relevant information:

(1) *historic and static factors,* including aspects of criminal history, previous violent behaviour, previous psychiatric history (including substance abuse, mental illness, and hostile personality disorders), adult adjustment with respect to close relationships and employment, and history of absconding from custody;

(2) *dynamic and clinical factors,* including impulsivity, antisocial attitudes and beliefs, anger and hostility, and individual symptoms of mental disorders such as delusions;

(3) *risk management factors,* reflecting aspects of the situation or environment rather than the person themselves – for example, release plan feasibility, access to professional and informal support, stressors, and idiosyncratic triggers for violence.

In relation to risk assessment for DSPD, a recent report by the British Psychological Society (BPS, 1999) stressed the need for multi-disciplinary, multi-agency involvement focusing on factors which have been shown to be empirically and functionally related to risk. Suggested data relevant for risk assessment includes: documentary evidence on previous history, validated risk assessments such as the PCL-R, psychometric assessments of personality, interview data, behavioural observation data, and psychophysiological assessments.

The Royal College of Psychiatrists Special Working Party on Clinical Assessment and Management of Risk have drawn up a list of general principles for managing risk in mental health settings. These are shown in Box. 5.1.

Where the identification of adolescents with the potential for ASPD is concerned, there are no clear guidelines, and different procedures have been developed depending on the context in which the young person finds themselves. Self-harm and suicide risk, by comparison, tend to be more readily identified and acted upon by services. However, risk assessment is a growing part of work in a wide range of agencies such as probation, social work and criminal justice, and, at the time of writing, the ASSET (an assessment schedule for use with all young offenders) is being introduced.

We have not attempted to provide an exhaustive review of the full range of issues implicated in designing and managing risk assessment. Recent reviews in this area include

Box 5.1   *General principles of managing risk in mental health settings*

1. Risk cannot be eliminated nor guaranteed.
2. Risk is dynamic and must be frequently reviewed.
3. Some risks are general, others are specific and have specific victims.
4. Interventions can increase risk as well as decrease it but good relationships make risk management easier.
5. Factors such as age, gender and ethnicity are not very useful in predicting risk in samples with mental disorders.
6. Clinicians should gather information from several sources.
7. Decisions should not be made by one person alone.
8. The outcomes must be shared but confidentiality respected.
9. Patients who are a risk to others are also likely to be a risk to themselves.

Source: Summarised from the Royal College of Psychiatrists Special Working Party on Clinical Assessment & Management of Risk (1996)

Douglas and others (1999), and Pritchard and Kemshall (1999). Some of the issues of concern are:

- who carries out the assessment (do they have to be clinicians)?
- use of informants
- how stable is the assessment – will it hold for months?
- reliability and validity (e.g. even 'hard' data like criminal offences are notoriously difficult to pin down)
- difference between current symptoms and future risk of antisocial behaviour.

For the purpose of the current report, a number of assessment tools are worth mentioning with respect to ASPD. The first is an assessment tool for measuring need rather than risk status in adolescence, which has recently been developed by a team at the Child and Adolescent Mental Health Services, Salford. Entitled the *Salford Needs Assessment Schedule for Adolescents* (S.NASA; Kroll et al, 1999) it identifies 21 areas of potential need, and assesses the significance of each need and how it might be met by services. The areas assessed involve material, familial, social, educational and psychiatric problems, including aggression and self-harm behaviour. The S.NASA is a potentially useful clinical decision-making tool for considering the appropriateness of a particular type of intervention for specified patient problems. However, the authors suggest that some personality disorders may require additional research instruments to identify the most appropriate intervention.

There are a number of other instruments that are concerned with the assessment of risk of future antisocial behaviour rather than assessments of need. The first is *Hare's PCL-R*, which has been used successfully to predict recidivism, and violent recidivism. It has been proposed as a primary instrument for guiding clinical assessments of risk for criminal recidivism and dangerousness (Hemphill et al, 1998). Although designed for use with adults, the measure has been used with adolescent offenders. In a study of 359 offenders (aged 12 to 18), 209 of whom had been convicted of a sexual crime, PCL-R scores were found to be predictive of later offending rates (Gretton et al, 1997). After an average follow-up period of six years, individuals with higher scores were significantly more likely to have re-offended, and their crimes were more likely to be sexual and/or violent in nature. This suggests that the PCL-R may be of use in prediction of future serious offending, although further studies are required to replicate this finding.

There are a limited number of measures designed specifically to assess future personality disorder or dangerousness in adolescents. However, there is a derivative of Hare's PCL-R for use with young people. The *Psychopathy Screening Device* has been developed for children, and is rated by parents and teachers (Frick, 1996; Frick et al, 1994). It aims to measure two dimensions related to psychopathy in adults. The first dimension includes 10 items that tap poor impulse control and conduct problem behaviour. The second dimension includes six items related to callous and unemotional interpersonal style. It is suggested that the latter factor can be used to identify those children with conduct disorder who are likely to develop ASPD in adulthood.

There is also a second instrument derived from the PCL-R (PCL:YV). It is an 18-item questionnaire, also designed to measure psychopathy amongst adolescents (Forth, Hart, & Hare, 1990; Forth, Kosson, & Hare, in press). However, it is too early to know what value this measure has in terms of the long-term prediction of adult outcomes such as ASPD.

Another instrument, designed specifically for use with children under the age of 12, is the *Early Assessment Risk List for Boys* (EARL-20B; Augimeri et al, 1998). It is a structured clinical decision-making guide, intended to help clinicians to assess violence risk in childhood. It comprises 20 items covering three sections: family factors (tapping the level of nurturance, support, and supervision in the home), child factors (concerning dimensions of sociability and spontaneity) and amenability factors (covering the resilience and competence of the child and family). Douglas and others (1999) suggest that the EARL-20B may be useful in identifying high-risk children in need of intensive intervention, and also for prioritising the needs of the individual child. A similar instrument for use with girls is currently being developed. Again, data concerning the instrument's predictive ability for adult outcomes such as ASPD are not known.

Future developments

Research on cognitive and emotional differences found in psychopaths may lead to the development of ways of identifying adolescents at risk of developing personality disorders. Lynam (1996) makes a number of suggestions regarding the means by which young psychopaths may be identified, and considers the potential usefulness of various laboratory tests and personality measures. They include, for example, card-playing or related tasks that have been used to demonstrate response modulation deficits associated with psychopathy (Milich et al, 1994). The development of tests assessing children's linguistic processing and use of language could also be a possibility, since abnormalities in these areas have been found in adult psychopaths (Hare & McPherson, 1984). It appears that the deep semantic and affective networks that connect cognitions are not well developed in psychopaths, based on the observation that psychopaths fail to appreciate the emotional significance of an event or experience, and have been shown to have difficulty processing or using the deep semantic meanings of language (Hare, 1998). Although highly speculative, they may be areas for future exploratory research to address.

Screening for risk within the context of existing service provision for high-risk adolescents

Psychiatric and psychological service provision for adolescents has evolved in a piecemeal fashion and does not follow any 'grand plan'. This is particularly the case where antisocial behaviour is concerned, as the involvement of other agencies is very likely (youth justice and welfare in particular). As a result, there are a number of confusions, overlaps and gaps. One particular issue concerns the definition of boundaries between childhood and adolescence. Some child and adolescent mental health services use the age of 16 or school leaving age as the upper limit, whilst many children's social services departments and education departments specify 18 or 19 as the upper limit.

Another issue arises from the complexity of the needs of high-risk adolescents. They often present with problems that require multiple agency involvement including mental health services, educational and social services, and custodial provision. Determining how and when which service should carry out assessment is not easy and it would be hard to systematise approaches across agencies. The issue is made more complicated by the variety of legal and administrative avenues available for handling children and young people with behavioural problems. Routes into services may vary considerably for young people with similar problems. Those who show disturbed behaviour from an early age, for example, may be picked up by educational and mental health services, whilst those whose behaviour extends into offending may be dealt with by youth justice services.

The rationale behind the intervention offered may also vary across time and context. The nature of services available for antisocial adolescents has evolved over the decades according to the prevailing concerns for welfare versus justice. A young person committing a serious offence may be seen as in need of punishment and detention, but at the same time may require special needs education, or psychological intervention for the effects of severe abuse or neglect, in which case custodial provision might be contraindicated. These concerns are also reflected in the mixed provision available for adolescents through the various administrative pathways.

In addition to the administrative pathways, there are also a number of legal options determining the nature and quality of diagnosis. Adolescents whose antisocial behaviour is a pre-cursor to adulthood ASPD may come under the provision of the *Mental Health Act, 1983* (indicating narrow psychiatric diagnosis), the *Children's Act, 1989* (demanding widely focused inter-agency assessment co-ordinated by a social worker), the *Crime and Disorder Act, 1998* (requiring intervention from Youth Offending Team professionals), or for a certain category of grave offender, the *Children and Young Persons Act, 1933* (often leading to a combination of the above forms of provision). Screening for risk for ASPD has, therefore, to be located in several legal and administrative contexts and requires completion by a varied group of professionals.

The nature of the risk assessment, and the consequent goal of the intervention offered, may vary depending on the identity of the service provider - hospital, youth justice, voluntary agency or local authority. It may involve prevention, rehabilitation or containment. Availability of resources also influences the nature of the individual's treatment. The treatment of young prisoners, for example, has been described as 'a lottery', dependent on the conditions of the establishment they find themselves in and the attitudes of the staff (Home Office, 1997). In a discussion of secure treatment settings for 'difficult' adolescents, Bullock , Little and Millham (1998) suggest that available services tend to be provision rather than needs led, and that what is required is: '...mechanisms for prioritising risk, setting out eligibility for services, ensuring that provision matches the needs of the child and identifying a single process leading to a continuum of interventions..' (p 18, Bullock et al, 1998).

Conclusions

The issue of assessment is closely linked to the issue of prevention and/or treatment. Once a method exists for identifying adolescents at high risk for developing a dangerous severe personality disorder, the question arises as to what the most appropriate intervention is.

However, our ability to predict who will become antisocial personality disordered remains relatively poor; measures achieve high sensitivity (i.e. correctly identifying those who will go on to develop ASPD), but with unacceptably low specificity, (i.e. mislabelling young people as high risk when they do not go on to develop ASPD). There appears to be no easy solution to this problem at present. Nevertheless, the remainder of the report considers some specific examples of interventions for severe antisocial behaviour, and implications for policy and research.

6   Research on interventions with adolescents

Introduction

In the discussion of interventions that follows, it is important to acknowledge from the outset that none of the interventions directly addresses the prevention of personality disorders, as there is a dearth of literature examining this issue. Instead, as through much of this report, we have drawn on findings from research based on offending and other forms of antisocial behaviour, which may overlap with personality disorder. Such research tends to be concerned with reducing offending behaviour rather than changing personality per se. Personality disorders are defined in terms of dysfunctional personality traits, some of which are found amongst offenders. It is these traits that interventions often aim to change (including, for example, hostility and impulse control).

Types of interventions

There are many factors that influence whether an individual will act in an antisocial way in a given situation. These include the opportunity for crime, perceptions of costs/rewards, situational 'press', emotional provocation, and individual liability (Rutter et al, 1997). Interventions to prevent antisocial acts therefore can take several forms, tackling any one of these contributing areas. Rutter et al (1998) describes three strategies for crime reduction with different aims. One involves tackling within-individual behavioural changes in selected individuals, the outcome of interest being a reduction in offending behaviour by a given individual. The second strategy is concerned with the aggregate level of crime, and aims to reduce the overall crime level within a group such as a school class. A third type of intervention focuses on specific forms of criminal acts (such as burglary) rather than offenders themselves. In the latter case the outcome of interest is a reduction in the number of crimes committed rather than the number of offenders.

The present report is selective in that it only describes interventions aimed at producing changes in antisocial behaviour at the individual level. The types of interventions discussed below concern 'developmental' prevention (Tonry & Farrington, 1995), designed to address the types of risk and protective factors that influence human development. Other forms of intervention may also be of use, and are discussed in depth elsewhere (see e.g. Hollin, 1995; Howell et al, 1995; Rutter et al, 1998; Stoff et al, 1997). These alternative forms of intervention include criminal justice interventions (involving the use of deterrence, incapacitation and rehabilitation carried out by law enforcement and judicial agencies), situation prevention (aimed at reducing the opportunities for offending), and community prevention (which targets social conditions and social institutions that influence offending) (Tonry & Farrington, 1995). The present selection of interventions was made for two reasons. First, the severity of cognitive and behavioural problems a person on a trajectory into adult ASPD is likely to be experiencing by the time they reach adolescence is such that interventions need to be highly tailored and individualised. Second, given the low base rate for ASPD, the cost-effectiveness of introducing an intervention aimed at a large population of adolescents in order to prevent a condition which affects so few must be considered questionable, as was discussed in Chapter 4.

Drug treatments are not discussed below, as they have recently been covered in a review of drug (and other) treatments for conduct disorder, to be published shortly (Fonagy et al, 2000). Fonagy and colleagues conclude that medication cannot be justified as the first line of treatment for conduct problems in children, although evidence suggests that psychostimulant medication in conjunction with psychosocial treatment may be beneficial.

Child-focused interventions

Cognitive and behavioural therapies
There are a number of interventions that use behavioural and cognitive techniques to modify the thoughts and actions of antisocial adolescents. Behavioural programmes can be distinguished from programmes that are cognitive-behavioural in orientation, and those that involve cognitive therapy alone. Behavioural programmes involve modification of behaviours by use of external rewards and punishments, whilst cognitive-behavioural approaches involve changing specific maladaptive or irrational thoughts that influence behaviour. In contrast, cognitive therapy uses psychotherapeutic techniques to address core schemata or specific cognitions that influence problems such as depression.

Behavioural programmes
Behavioural programmes focus on specific aspects of behaviour rather than on the psychological states that may underpin them, and attempt to alter the behaviours by changing the antecedents and consequences involved. Such programmes have traditionally taken the form of token economies, in which points obtained through good behaviour are

exchanged for privileges. Early studies of a token economy programme used with adolescent offenders showed short-term benefits were not sustained in the long term (Cohen & Filipczak, 1971). Whilst the treated group had lower re-offending rates in the first two years, at final follow-up after three years there were no significant group differences, although academic improvements were maintained in the treated group.

In another behavioural study, Moyes, Tennent and Bedford (1985) examined the effects of a token economy, social skills training, and contingency management on outcomes for a group of 78 adolescents with antisocial behaviour and a comparison group of 63 adolescents with similar problems who were not treated. At two-year follow-up, the treated group displayed less physical aggression and temper outbursts and less self-mutilation, but rates of involvement with the police did not differ to those of the untreated group. There were significant differences in the histories of the treated and untreated groups at the start of the study that may have influenced outcomes, and thus limit the value of the results. Many studies of token economies are methodologically weak, lacking, for example, long-term follow-ups or properly matched control groups. Hence firm conclusions regarding the effectiveness of this approach cannot be drawn.

Cognitive therapy

Originally conceived by Beck, cognitive therapy for the treatment of emotional disorders has been developed in order to treat adults with personality disorders (Beck et al, 1990). Cognitive therapy addresses symptoms such as behavioural problems and also the underlying schemata, or psychological structures, that maintain them. Unlike psychoanalytic theorists, cognitive therapists believe that the cognitive schemata underpinning the irrational thoughts and behaviour are accessible to conscious appraisal. Beck and colleagues (op cit) see the task of cognitive therapy with psychopaths as developing greater awareness of the feelings and rights of others, since moral reasoning and cognitive functioning are thought to be under-developed in this group.

There are no controlled studies on the efficacy of cognitive therapy (Blackburn, 2000). Most reports of cognitive therapy with personality disordered patients take the form of case studies, and are confined to patients with avoidant or borderline personality disorders. In a single case study, Blackburn (1993) reported on the successful use of cognitive therapy in combination with skills training in the treatment of an adult psychopath. Its effectiveness in controlled trials with adolescents with potential personality disorder is not known.

Cognitive–behavioural programmes

The cognitive-behavioural approach involves training in one or more areas of skills deficit, including social skills, problem-solving skills, anger management and moral reasoning. The rationale for using such skills deficit approaches is based on several observations and assumptions suggesting, for example, that delinquent adolescents show immaturity in moral reasoning tasks, and that adolescents lacking in appropriate social skills revert to antisocial means of achieving their goals. Training can involve use of role-play, videotape modelling and feedback, discussion in-groups or individually, homework tasks, etc.

Dialectical Behaviour Therapy (DBT; Linehan, 1994) is a particular form of cognitive-behavioural treatment that has been used in the treatment of personality disorders in adults. It combines cognitive-behavioural problem-solving strategies with supportive techniques involving reflection, empathy, and acceptance. Positive results for this form of treatment have been demonstrated with parasuicidal women with borderline personality disorder in terms of reduced rates of self-injury and hospitalisation (Linehan, 1994). However, its effectiveness with ASPD, and on severe antisocial behaviour in adolescents is unknown. Its applicability to the problem of antisocial behaviour is questionable given that it was not designed to address this type of behaviour.

The use of cognitive-behavioural therapy has intuitive appeal given that it addresses some of the core features of ASPD such as acting on impulse, showing aggression, and lacking remorse. In a review of strategies for intervening with offenders, McGuire (1995) concludes that cognitive-behavioural approaches offer much promise. One particular form of cognitive-behavioural therapy, involving moral reasoning education programmes based on the cognitive-developmental theory of Kohlberg (discussed in Chapter 4), is reported as effecting a wide range of changes in juvenile offenders (e.g. Rosenkoetter, Landman, & Mazak, 1986).

When studies have failed to demonstrate the effectiveness of such intervention programmes, a number of reasons may be involved. First, learned skills and changes in attitude may not always translate into altered behaviour, and second, when there are changes in behaviour, these may not generalise beyond the treatment setting. A study of social skills training in adolescent delinquents, for example, found that treatment gains assessed at the end of the 12 training sessions were maintained when tested again three months later, but these improvements were not evident in ratings from observers in other settings such as in family, school or social relationships (Spence & Marzillier, 1981).

Another difficulty with changes in behaviour resulting from cognitive-behavioural therapy is that the changes may not represent enduring modification of antisocial behaviours. Often studies have either failed to measure long-term outcomes or else have shown initially positive results which have not lasted. An example of the latter is a study by Guerra and Slaby (1990) which showed that incarcerated offenders who completed a 'viewpoints training program' were less likely to be rated by staff as aggressive or impulsive compared with a no-treatment group and a placebo group. However, at 24 months post-treatment no group differences were found in terms of the numbers of offenders violating their parole.

It has been suggested that the short-term nature of many cognitive-behavioural programmes may render them insufficient to bring about changes in individuals with severe antisocial behaviours or personality disorders, where the problem is pervasive and persistent (Dolan & Coid, 1993). It is acknowledged that such approaches generally only attempt to treat a specific aspect of behaviour or attitude, and as such, may have a role to play in short-term management of disruptive behaviour rather than intervention for psychopathy (op cit).

Multi-modal programmes

There are a number of cognitive-behavioural programmes that combine skills training in several different areas. Multi-modal treatments are more likely to tackle the multiple causes of severe behavioural problems, as well as providing a sufficient 'dosage' to impact on severe and chronic antisocial behaviour (Kazdin, 1996). Unfortunately, there have been few evaluations of their effectiveness, and the programmes that have been evaluated show mixed results. For example, an 'Aggression Replacement Training' (ART) programme combining social skills training, anger control and moral reasoning training produced differences in some outcomes but not others. Juvenile offenders who took part in ART showed improvements in social behaviours, moral reasoning and impulsivity when compared to a no-treatment group, but at follow-up did not differ from controls in terms of externalising behaviours (Goldstein & Glick, 1994). However, positive results in terms of recidivism rates were found for a similar treatment programme combining social skills training, anger management, moral reasoning training and problem-solving skills training used with incarcerated adolescent offenders (Leeman, Gibbs & Fuller, 1993). Recidivism rates at one-year follow-up were 15 per cent for the treatment group compared with 41 per cent for the control group.

Many of the evaluation studies of cognitive-behavioural therapy have been conducted in North America rather than Britain. However, a randomised controlled trial is currently being conducted in London, comparing a multi-component cognitive-behavioural package with a counselling programme (Baruch, 2000). It is being carried out at the Brandon Centre (formerly the London Youth Advisory Centre), a charitable organisation providing counselling and psychotherapy for young people aged between 12 and 25. The study aims to reduce re-offending amongst a group of persistent young offenders in the 14 to 16 age group, whose behaviour fulfils DSM-IV criteria for conduct disorder. Referrals to the treatment trial are made via youth offending teams as part of a supervision order. Participants are randomly allocated to one of two interventions. The first involves a manualised cognitive behaviour programme delivered twice weekly in 20 sessions. It addresses deficits in problem-solving skills, anger management, social perspective taking and moral reasoning. It also incorporates lessons learned at the Brandon Centre from engaging difficult-to-treat young people in psychoanalytic psychotherapy. The second intervention also comprises 20 sessions delivered on a twice-weekly basis, and provides the young people with counselling. Follow-up sessions are also available to participants on a once a week basis for a further six months.

The study uses standardised measures to assess participants on a number of outcomes (including rate of reconviction), with data from multiple sources including teachers, youth justice workers, and the young people themselves. Participants are assessed at entry to treatment, at the end of treatment, and then one year later. Data are still being collected, but results so far suggest that treatment compliance is relatively good. The study is significant as there are few, if any, randomised controlled trials in the UK examining multi-component packages for use with this client group. Preliminary findings are expected to be available later in 2001. Whilst such multi-modal packages hold more promise for improving outcome, it is still too early to specify the number or sequence or type of skills training programmes required to maximise effectiveness, or to know whether they are sufficiently powerful to prevent antisocial or other personality disorders in adulthood.

Psychotherapy

Psychotherapy often forms part of the milieu therapy offered in residential settings, and also forms an important part of the therapeutic community approach (described later). Psychodynamic approaches to ASPD aim to provide patients with insight into their underlying personality disturbance, and, by means of the close alliance with the therapist, allow exploration of the defence mechanisms that underpin their maladaptive behaviour. Some of the central features of psychotherapy, including the potential for insight and the need to form a trusting relationship with the therapist, are the very features that lead some clinicians to conclude that psychotherapy is contraindicated in the case of psychopaths or individuals with personality disorder. Resistant and poorly motivated clients do not respond well to psychotherapy (e.g. Strupp & Hadley, 1979), and individuals with personality disorders tend to fall into this group. Bailey (1996) points out that previous frequent and severe aggression, low intelligence, and a poor capacity for insight hamper the chances of effectiveness of psychotherapy with violent young people. She observes that in such a disadvantaged group 'therapeutic gains come slowly', and suggests that psychotherapy should not be considered as the primary means of treatment.

Studies evaluating the use of psychotherapy with adolescent in-patients have produced some positive but limited results. For example, an early study that examined the effects of group therapy in institutionalised delinquent girls showed that there were greater improvements in self-esteem, self-adjustment, attitudes and social functioning compared to a no-treatment group (Truax, Wargo, & Silber, 1966). However, scores on a measure of emotional stability indicated that they were still delinquency-prone. Another study of adolescent girls in a borstal showed that group therapy led to greater improvements in scores on personality, attitudinal and behavioural measures when compared with counselling or no treatment (Taylor, 1967). Although there were no group differences in re-offending rates, girls in the treatment group tended to commit less serious crimes than they had done previously. The study involved very small numbers of subjects (33 in total) and had a relatively short follow-up period of only 26 weeks. Further studies are required with larger samples and longer follow-up periods in order to evaluate the effectiveness of psychotherapy with high-risk adolescents.

Therapeutic communities

Therapeutic communities (TCs) are types of residential settings that offer a variety of therapeutic techniques, including the psychotherapeutic methods described above. TCs vary greatly in terms of their philosophical orientation, therapeutic techniques employed, and role of staff. Generally they are 'insight' orientated, and involve a great deal of intensive group therapy in which participants are encouraged to explore 'subjective experience and personal values' (p285; Harris, Rice and Cormier, 1994). Treatment may feature psychodynamic counselling, group encounter sessions, and defence-disrupting therapy. An important principle in any TC programme is that of 'community as doctor' (Rapoport, 1960). Hence patients, referred to as 'residents', are active participants in their own treatment, and share responsibility for day-to-day running of the TC with staff members.

Studies evaluating the effects of TCs have most often examined their use with adults rather than adolescents, and mixed results are reported. This may partly be due to the wide variety of institutions that describe themselves as TCs, the content of the treatment offered, and the nature of the client group involved as well as the design of the evaluations themselves. The positive effects of TCs include improvement in psychological measures such as hostility, and social introversion (Gunn & Robertson, 1982; Miller, 1982), as well as reduction in serious incidents during incarceration (Cooke, 1989), and lower reconviction rates (Marshall, 1997). However, some long-term studies indicate that TC treatment makes little difference to recidivism rates (Robertson & Gunn, 1987), and may even make them worse (Rice, Harris, & Cormier, 1992).

Findings from studies of adults in TCs highlight several features of the intervention that affect success rate. For example, a lack of structure within the therapeutic programme, a reliance on clinical intuition (Wilson, 1997), as well as absence of skills-based or behavioural interventions, have been cited as reasons for their reduced success with some individuals. On the other hand, longer stays and voluntary participation in the programme appear to be beneficial for outcome (Rice et al, 1992), suggesting that TC treatment may be more successful with those who want to be treated (Dolan & Coid, 1993).

There are few reports evaluating the use of TCs with adolescents, although at the time of writing a number of TCs that form part of the Charterhouse group are being evaluated. This is an umbrella organisation that promotes and supports several residential homes for adolescents run on TC principles using a psychodynamic approach. Member organisations endeavour to create an environment and relationships that allow residents to relearn (and learn anew) about the relationship between their own thoughts and feelings and their experience of other people. A number of key principles are adhered to, which emphasise (1) attachment – engendering a sense of belonging and personal value; (2) containment – allowing expression of emotional distress but maintaining boundaries and expectations; (3) communication – encouraging openness and enquiry; (4) involvement – in which all aspects of daily life are of concern to staff and residents; and (5) responsibility – acknowledging that residents and staff have contributions to make to the community. For many of the children and adolescents, entry to the TC follows after a series of placement breakdowns. Treatment typically lasts from two to four years, and is usually carried out in a rurally located group home varying in size from five to 72 residents, although some work is carried out in day settings. Dropout rates are reported to be relatively low. The approach is holistic in so far as the social, attachment, educational and physical needs of the children are addressed.

A study reporting on the effectiveness of TCs with adolescents identified a group of mainly older boys who were less likely to be helped by the TC. They had problems with physical aggression, had previously offended, and had spent time in residential care (Fitzgerald, 1990). TCs, therefore, may be more effective with some types of clients than with others, although further evaluation studies are required to assess their effectiveness.

A study based at the 'Young Persons Unit' (YPU) at Broadmoor Hospital, which incorporates aspects of a therapeutic community model within a maximum security setting, drew similar conclusions regarding the mixed success of the TC approach. Reiss, Grubin and Meux (1996) reported on outcomes for 49 young psychopaths treated at the YPU, whose average age at time of admission was 19 years. Treatment lasted for an average of four years, and involved interpretative group therapy, as well as structured group sessions on topics concerning sex education, social skills, assertiveness, feelings and empathy, anger management, relationships, self-awareness, moral dilemmas, and families. Individual psychodynamic therapy and behavioural therapy were also used. The majority of patients also took part in general education and occupational activities.

Patients' functioning (in terms of recidivism and a variety of social factors) was assessed at two years following admission, two years before discharge, and finally following discharge. Results showed that over half of the sample was settled in the community following discharge, and appeared to be socially integrated. However, 20 per cent (10) of patients had re-offended, and eight of the 10 individuals had done so in the community. Four had committed serious offences after they had left Broadmoor, including two homicides, indicating that despite lengthy, intensive treatment a minority still continued to pose a danger. Poorer prognosis in terms of re-offending was predicted by a previous history of sexual offending, and lower intelligence. None of the patients who rated as having a good social outcome re-offended, with good social outcome defined as having established friendships or a relationship, settled employment and accommodation, and an absence of substance abuse. The authors concluded that young patients with severe personality disorder could be successfully treated at YPU, but that consideration needed to be given to the suitability of patients for this type of treatment, given that those with a history of sexual offending were most likely to re-offend. They also recommend that successful social integration within the community after discharge may help prevent future offending. The lack of a comparison group is a serious methodological shortcoming in the report, however.

Further studies of TCs are required to disentangle the particular features of this approach that affect treatment outcome. It is difficult to tell if there is anything specifically beneficial about TCs over and above any other treatment programme that is characterised by lengthy treatment, treatment integrity, and a holistic, multi-modal approach. An early investigation of young offenders by Craft, Stephenson & Granger (1964), for example, concluded that a TC was no more beneficial than the comparison treatment involving an authoritarian programme with individual therapy. In this study, recidivism rates were compared amongst young probationers who had been randomly assigned to a TC or the alternative treatment. At three years post-treatment, the TC group showed higher rates of re-offending and had committed more serious offences when compared to the comparison group. Participation in the TC programme was not voluntary, and, if findings from adults can be generalised to adolescents, lack of voluntary participation may have significantly contributed to the failure of the intervention.

Given the heterogeneous nature of TCs, combined with a lack of well-designed evaluative studies in this area, it is difficult to draw conclusions about their effectiveness with adolescents. However, it appears that under certain circumstances, certain types of clients may benefit from this approach. With further studies it may be possible to delineate more precisely both the key features of the TC and characteristics of the client that optimise the effects of the treatment.

Parent-focused interventions

Parenting training programmes

Parenting training programmes usually involve teaching parents specific child management skills. One approach is based on social learning theory, and helps parents to monitor their child's behaviour more effectively, to positively reinforce socially acceptable behaviour in the child, and to discipline effectively. Antisocial young people and adults with ASPD are likely to have experienced either lax or harsh discipline, or abusive parenting in childhood.

Generally, parent-training programmes are less successful with adolescents than with younger children. One reason may be that the influence of parents diminishes as the child enters adolescence. This has been suggested by a number of researchers who highlight the role of the peer group as a dominant influence once adolescence has been reached (e.g. Allen & Land, 1999). A study by Riley and Shaw (1985), for example, found that in addition to poor parental supervision, extra-familial influences such as peer group were associated with antisocial behaviour.

Another reason for the lack of effectiveness of parental training programmes with older children may be that symptoms tend to be more severe and behaviour patterns more entrenched by the time of adolescence. This was the conclusion drawn by Coleman, Henricson and Roker (1999) in a review of youth justice parenting interventions. Such interventions were found to be least likely to succeed with early-onset antisocial behaviour rather than adolescent-limited antisocial behaviour, creating doubts about effectiveness in the prevention of ASPD.

This suggestion is also borne out by results from several US studies. Patterson and his colleagues at the Oregan Social Learning Centre, for example, have tested a model of parenting which was originally based on their successful programme for younger children (Bank et al, 1991). They have devised an extended parent management training programme that involves increased parental monitoring, the use of punishment procedures such as restricting free time, targeting of specific behaviours associated with delinquency (such as poor school attendance and deviant peer group membership), the use of behavioural contracts, and parental reporting of offending behaviour to the juvenile justice authorities.

A study reported by Bank and colleagues investigated the effects of this modified parent training compared to a 'treatment as usual' group on offending rates for chronic juvenile offenders (Bank et al, 1991). Initial results were promising: rates of offending were reduced in both groups, but in addition, the individuals in the parent training group spent less time in institutions during the first two years of the follow-up. However, after three years there were no group differences. It has been suggested that parent management training may only be helpful in reducing adolescent antisocial behaviour as an additional component within family therapy models (Brunck, 1999), or that parent training in combination with cognitive-behavioural therapy for the child may bring about better results than either treatment alone (Webster-Stratton & Hammond, 1997). On its own it may be too brief or lack sufficient intensity to influence persistent and severe antisocial adolescent behaviour, particularly the type that may develop into ASPD.

Family-focused interventions

Multisystemic treatment (MST)

Multisystemic treatment (Henggeler & Borduin, 1990; Henggeler et al, 1998) is an individualised treatment model in which families set goals and collaborate with practitioners in designing and implementing interventions to meet these goals. It is aimed at youths engaged in serious antisocial behaviour, who are likely to have received a diagnosis of conduct disorder or oppositional defiant disorder, although the precise diagnosis may not have direct bearing on clinical decision-making. The age range of clients is 12-15 years, although 16 or 17-year-olds may be considered, and there may also be exceptions to the lower age limit. The practitioner's task is to work closely with the family in identifying factors contributing towards the young person's problem behaviours as well as identifying factors reflecting systematic strengths that might be used to attenuate the problems. The primary goal of treatment is to reduce rates of antisocial behaviour. Since there are likely to be multiple determinants of antisocial behaviour, the treatment programme has the potential to intervene at individual, family, peer, school, and neighbourhood levels.

The theoretical basis of MST lies in a combination of general systems theory (von Bertalanffy, 1968) and the theory of social ecology (Bronfenbrenner, 1979). Nine treatment principles have been delineated, and include: the need to understand the relationship between the identified problems and the broader systemic context; to develop action-orientated interventions which require daily or weekly effort by the family, and are targeted at specific problems; to target sequences of behaviour within and between multiple systems that maintain the behaviour; to evaluate the intervention's effectiveness from multiple perspectives; to build on positive strengths and promote responsible behaviour using developmentally appropriate means; and finally, to empower the youth and family so that long-term benefits are derived.

MST is predominantly conducted via a home-based model of service delivery in order to facilitate changes in the 'social ecology' of youth and family. It provides intensive treatment over a four to six month period per family, depending on the seriousness of the problems involved. Each therapist has a low caseload, typically involving three to six families, and has daily contact with them. Therapists work in small teams of three to four practitioners, and are available 24 hours per day, seven days per week (either personally or else another team member). Close supervision of therapists is seen as an essential part of the process, as research has shown that effectiveness of MST is reliant on MST treatment integrity.

Several randomised control trials involving MST have been conducted in the US. Overall, MST has been successful in a variety of contexts and settings. A study of violent and chronic juvenile offenders (Henggeler et al, 1993), for example, compared outcomes of MST to the usual services provided by the Department of Juvenile Justice (DJJ) amongst a group of violent and/or chronic juvenile offenders. There was greater improvement in family functioning (involving more family cohesion and reduced conflict) amongst MST youths compared to DJJ treated youths. Results also showed that MST was significantly better at reducing re-arrest rates, and length of time incarcerated. Almost two and a half years later, the differences between groups in recidivism rates were maintained. MST also led to significant reductions in self-reported drug use.

In another randomised control trial involving 200 juvenile offenders, the short and long-term effects of MST were compared with results for office-based, individual counselling (Borduin et al, 1995). As in the study by Henggeler and others, there was greater improvement in family functioning amongst offenders receiving MST compared with individual counselling.

Four years after treatment, MST youths were significantly less likely than counselled youths to be re-arrested were. Where re-arrest did occur, the MST youths were less likely to have been arrested for violent crimes (such as rape, attempted rape, sexual assault, aggravated assault, or assault/battery). Evidence for a dose-response effect in support of a causal effect for MST was evident when the re-arrest rates were compared for those youths who had dropped out part way through treatment. Re-arrest rates for youths who completed MST were 22 per cent, compared with rates of 47 per cent for MST drop-outs, 71 per cent for youths completing individual counselling, and 88 per cent for counselling drop-outs. MST also led to a significant reduction in the number of drug-related arrests. Adolescents' age, race, gender, social class, or pre-treatment arrest history did not moderate the effectiveness of MST.

The importance of treatment integrity for maximising the effectiveness of the intervention was demonstrated by a randomised control study of violent and chronic juvenile offenders in a rural setting (Henggeler et al, 1997). The effects of MST were compared with the usual DJJ services for violent and chronic adolescent offenders. However, the MST programme was adjusted so that the usual weekly consultations between therapists and MST experts were cut in order to reduce costs. Results showed that MST was effective in improving adolescent symptomology at post-treatment and, at 1.7 year follow-up, in decreasing length of time spent incarcerated. However, MST had made relatively little difference to the level of criminal activity in which the adolescents were engaged. Further analysis showed that adherence to the MST treatment principles was an important predictor of the level of criminal behaviour. It was concluded that clinical outcomes for serious juvenile offenders were directly related to the integrity of the MST implementation.

Limitations

A criticism of the clinical studies evaluating MST is that each was directed by one of the developers of MST. Evaluation by independent investigators is required, and is underway. In addition, there are no data available on longer-term follow-up of treated youths beyond four to five years post-treatment. Aside from the methodological problems of the evaluation studies, it is also important to consider the potential limitations of MST in terms of suitable client groups and the mode of service delivery. Young people are deemed to be unsuitable for the programme if they live in a group home, residential setting, or other situations outside the family. Those living with at least one adult caregiver are accepted, whether the caregiver is an older sibling, grandparent, aunt, uncle, or friend of the family. There must also be willingness on the part of the family to co-operate, which may not always be forthcoming. These factors may also potentially bias results of the evaluation studies in so far as those most likely to respond to treatment may be selected into the experimental group.

The possibility of utilising MST in a clinic-based setting rather than home-delivery mode is being considered, and a range of MST services are being provided within neighbourhood locations for youths where less intensive family work is required. It is too early to know whether the service will be as effective when delivered in this way. In terms of client groups, sex offenders are not usually accepted for treatment because the effectiveness of MST has not been demonstrated with this group (although projects are currently underway). Currently there are a number of studies being conducted using MST with a series of different client groups, including substance-abusing parents of young children, and abused and neglected children.

Overall, MST appears to be a moderately effective intervention for youths with severe antisocial behaviour problems, although independent research has yet to confirm this. It builds on positive aspects of the young person's attributes and situation rather than simply rectifying deficits, and may therefore be drawing on factors that prove to be protective in the long-term. MST is an expensive treatment, but is argued to be cost-effective. Washington State Institute for Public Policy calculates that the MST programme costs about $4,500 per participant, and lowers the subsequent level of felony offending by 44 per cent (WSIPP, 1998). It calculates that this reduction in crime would save taxpayers $12,381 per participant in future criminal justice system costs, thus making a total saving to the taxpayer of $7,881 for every high risk juvenile offender placed on the programme. In addition, it estimates that $13,982 in future out-of-pocket costs paid by crime victims can be avoided with the MST programme. To our knowledge, MST has not been tested in the UK.

Treatment foster care (TFC)

A limitation of the MST programme described above is that the client must be part of a family that is willing to participate in the programme. Young people with antisocial behaviour may find themselves living away from their family in residential care settings or group homes in which MST would not be applicable. Under such circumstances, treatment foster care (TFC) may represent an alternative to traditional residential intervention. Although not strictly a family-focused intervention, since it applies to youths that would otherwise be living in residential group homes, TFC is nevertheless an extension of parent-mediated programmes. It involves foster parents playing a central role in a programme of treatment and rehabilitation of the young person. An example of this approach reported by Chamberlain and colleagues (Chamberlain, 1994; Chamberlain & Reid, 1994) uses elements of the Oregon Social Learning Centre model. Foster parents are recruited and screened from community-based families, and take part in pre-service training. Throughout the intervention they are given ongoing support and supervision in the form of individual and group meetings, and 24-hour crisis support. Individual therapy is given to the child in the form of problem-solving skills and anger management training. Therapy is also undertaken with the child's biological family. The foster parents work in conjunction with several services including therapists, probation services, and educational services to manage the day-to-day behaviour of the young person in the home and in the community.

Studies evaluating TFC show promising results. A two-year follow-up of a small sample of 16 chronic juvenile offenders who were offered TFC showed that their re-incarceration rate was only 50 per cent compared to 94 per cent for a matched group who received 'treatment as usual'. The number of days spent incarcerated was also lower in the experimental group in each year following treatment. Recently Chamberlain and Moore (1998) reported preliminary findings of a randomised control trial involving 79 12-18-year-old chronic offenders who took part in TFC or else were placed in a residential group setting. Analysis of preliminary data from 68 subjects at six-month follow-up showed that there were substantial reductions in self-reported delinquency behaviour, rates of incarceration, and frequency of running away. Results for those who had completed the 12-month follow-up also showed that 31 per cent of the TFC group had run away compared with 58 per cent of the control group. There was also a significant difference in the length of time the young people had spent incarcerated (53 days versus 129 days).

A meta-analysis of 40 studies involving TFC in various forms revealed moderate reductions in behaviour problems and improvement in social skills (Reddy & Pfeiffer, 1997), with one of the most successful programmes being that of Chamberlain and colleagues, described above. Figures from the Washington State Institute for Public Policy (WSIPP, 1998) indicate that the treatment is cost-effective, saving the taxpayer on average $5,815 per programme participant. Whilst the TFC approach has produced positive results, many of the evaluation studies have involved small numbers and short follow-up periods. Larger samples with longer follow-ups are required to ascertain how substantial and sustained the effects of this approach may be.

Functional family therapy (FFT)

Family therapy can take various forms, but typically involves a trained therapist working with multiple family members as a group. The intervention aims to influence family management practices, family conflict and antisocial behaviour, and to facilitate effective family interaction, family bonding, and clear standards of behaviour. The functional family therapy approach adopted by Alexander and Parsons (1973, 1982) addresses patterns of interaction and communication between family members, and combines a behavioural approach with a family systems approach. Cognitive methods are initially used to identify the expectations, attributions and systemic processes that need to change. After this, predominantly behavioural methods are used to initiate change, involving training in communications skills, drawing up behavioural contracts, and contingency monitoring.

Several studies have shown promising results for functional family therapy. Alexander and Parsons compared the effects of family functional therapy with psychodynamic family interventions, attention placebo and no-treatment control groups in families with delinquents. Improvement in family interaction and reduced recidivism rates were superior in the functional family therapy group compared to any of the other groups at the two-year follow-up. For example, recidivism rates were 26 per cent for the functional family therapy condition compared with 47 per cent in the client-centred counselling group, 73 per cent in the psychodynamic counselling group, and 50 per cent in the no-treatment group. In addition, a significantly lower rate of offending in siblings was also found in the family functional therapy group. Other studies testing variations of the functional family therapy approach have generally found it to be effective, for example, when adapted to include a remedial education and job training component (Barton et al, 1985), and also in a rural context, using a longer treatment period and closer training and supervision of the therapist (Gordon, Graves, & Arbuthnot, 1995). Whilst these results are extremely encouraging, there have been methodological weaknesses that reduce the robustness of the results. These studies require replication with larger samples of more severely antisocial youth in order to test the value of this intervention.

Meta-analyses

The aggregation of research studies in the form of meta-analyses has provided an overview of the types of treatments that have the greatest effects. The results of such analyses should be viewed with caution due to the varying conceptual and methodological approaches they encompass. The outcomes under investigation can vary, for example, from improved self-esteem to recidivism rates, with much smaller effect sizes found for the latter (Garrett, 1985). However, it is encouraging that broadly similar conclusions have emerged from the individual studies cited above as from these analyses.

Lipsey (1992, 1995) carried out a meta-analysis of 443 intervention studies aimed at reducing juvenile delinquency. Results showed that within the juvenile justice system in North America, the greatest reduction in delinquency was achieved by the more specific and structured programmes such as those involving skills training with behavioural techniques, and also treatments that were multi-modal. Treatment intensity, involving longer treatment with more frequent contacts, was also found to relate to better outcomes. Lipsey's definition of treatment also included criminal sanctions such as diversion, boot camps, probation and parole. Negative effects (i.e. an increase in offending) were seen in approaches that favoured deterrence (such as exposing juveniles to fear-inducing conditions in prison).

A meta-analysis of mainly juvenile studies reported on the effectiveness of 'appropriate' and 'inappropriate' services (Andrews et al, 1996). The appropriateness of treatment was decided on the basis of three principles: (1) delivery of services to higher risk cases rather than low risk; (2) targeting of criminogenic needs (defined as antisocial attitudes, peer associations, substance dependence, deficits in social skills, self-control, and self-management); (3) the use of styles and modes of treatment that matched the client need and learning styles. The 'appropriate' category included delivering behavioural programmes and structured non-behavioural programmes targeting specific needs and deficits in high-risk individuals, whilst the 'inappropriate' category included services to lower risk individuals, involving non-directive, relationship-dependent, psychodynamic therapy; milieu therapy; and group approaches emphasising communication. An overall effect size of .63 was found for the former compared with an effect size of .20 for the latter. (Effect size usually refers to Cohen's d, and reflects the difference between the means of the treatment and control groups, expressed in standard deviation units.) The authors stress the need to consider under which conditions which programme will work, driven by theoretical knowledge of the causes of crime and the processes influencing behaviour.

The *Misspent Youth* report produced by Audit Commission (1996) contains a number of recommendations regarding ways of tackling youth crime. Drawing on the work of Andrews (1995), the report outlines several promising targets for intervening to reduce offending behaviour, with emphasis placed on 'dynamic' factors that directly relate to offending. Factors that do not directly relate to offending behaviour are seen as less promising targets, such as enhancing self-esteem, or focusing on emotional and personal problems that are not linked to criminal acts. Promising targets include:

- changing antisocial attitudes
- changing antisocial feelings
- reducing antisocial peer associations
- promoting family affection and communication
- promoting family supervision and monitoring
- promoting identification and association with anti-criminal role models
- increasing self-control, self-management and problem-solving skills

- replacing the skills of lying, stealing, and aggression with more pro-social alternatives
- reducing chemical dependencies
- rewarding non-criminal activities in family, academic, work and leisure settings
- ensuring that the client can recognise risky situations and has a plan for dealing with them and
- providing those who have chronic psychiatric problems with appropriate help.

The degree to which the results of the meta-analyses described above may be applied to interventions for potentially personality disordered individuals is unknown. Given the resistance to treatment of the most severe antisocial youth, there is likely to be less improvement in outcome for this group compared to the broader range of youth with antisocial behaviour. We know, for example, that interventions aimed at increasing a parent's supervision and monitoring of their adolescent offspring do not, on their own at least, impact on young people with severe antisocial behaviour. Hence several of the promising targets may need to be simultaneously tackled in adolescents who are at highest risk.

The difficulty of intervening with very high-risk individuals is emphasised by the results of a meta-analysis of treatment studies for psychopathy in adults by Garrido, Esteban, and Molero (1996). They found that psychopaths (defined by a number of measures) did less well in a variety of treatment settings than non-psychopaths. However, they also found that pre-post comparisons on behavioural and psychological tests showed positive effects for younger individuals, suggesting that early identification is beneficial to longer-term outlook.

Even if analyses demonstrate a positive effect for a particular type of treatment, the development of policy based on such results needs to proceed with caution. In a review of treatment for offenders, Simon (1998) warns against over-optimism in the interpretation of effect sizes produced from meta-analyses. He suggests that unlike medical decisions taken on the basis of small effect sizes, making criminal justice decisions on the basis of such results may compromise public safety if it leads to the release of dangerous offenders into the community.

Matching interventions to clients

Given the lack of conclusive evidence regarding the effectiveness of any single intervention for severe antisocial behaviour in adolescents, there is a need to consider the interaction between treatment components and personality characteristics. This has been stressed by a number of authors (e.g. Andrews et al, 1996; Bullock et al, 1998; Offord & Reitsma-Street,

1983; Rutter, 1982). In a discussion of interventions for adult psychopaths, Losel (1998) recommends that styles and modes of treatment should be matched to the styles and abilities of clients. Tolan and Gorman-Smith (1997) also recommend that evaluation studies must test for whom and under what circumstances a particular intervention is effective.

The view that adolescents with severe antisocial behaviour constitute a mixed group with differing needs for treatment has also been highlighted recently in a study of personality characteristics in adolescent offenders. Steiner, Cauffman and Duxbury (1999) examined personality characteristics of incarcerated juvenile offenders, and developed a typology based on scores of self-reported 'distress' and 'restraint' using the Weinberger Adjustment Inventory (WAI; Weinberger, 1997). 'Distress' involved four affective dimensions including anxiety, depression, low well being, and low self-esteem. 'Restraint' also involved four dimensions: tapping impulse control, suppression of aggression, responsibility, and consideration. These personality traits were predictive of criminal activity in the follow-up period, even after controlling for criminological predictors such as age at incarceration, length of stay, number of previous offences, and seriousness of committing offence. Of the individuals who scored low on distress and low on restraint, 89 per cent were re-arrested during the 4.5 year follow-up, compared with 44 per cent of those who scored high on distress and high on restraint. Steiner and others (1999) suggest that personality characteristics may be useful tools for sub-typing individuals in order to tailor treatment packages. They suggest, for example, that individuals with high distress and low restraint may respond best to structure and behaviour management, and that their high distress levels may relate to some affective disturbance that could be treated with drugs. The authors conclude that 'juvenile delinquents are a heterogeneous population in terms of personality features…We may be able to use this understanding to target specific domains of functioning to develop more effective intervention strategies' (p 256; Steiner et al, 1999).

Summary and conclusions

Table 6.1 lists the main interventions that we have discussed in this chapter and suggests some of the limitations associated with each in terms of the application to ASPD. In the last 25 years there has been a gradual, cautiously optimistic shift in opinion regarding the effectiveness of interventions with delinquents. In 1974, it was possible for Martinson to conclude that 'nothing works'. Today there is rigorous enquiry into 'what works?' However, where interventions for the relatively small group of potentially disordered adolescents is concerned, there remains a paucity of robust scientific studies. It is clear from the studies discussed in this chapter that no single intervention appears to be conclusively effective in halting the progression of severely antisocial personality into adult personality disorder. Of the interventions reviewed, those that are child-, parent- and family-focused, or combinations of these, seem to offer most promise. However, further studies are required to test their impact more rigorously, and to establish their effectiveness with adolescents at highest risk.

Table 6.1: **Summary of child-parent and family-focused interventions that could potentially be applied to ASPD**

Type of intervention	Limitation
With some positive results	
Multisystemic therapy	Family must be willing/co-operative
	No independent evaluation results yet
Treatment foster care	Unclear what components are effective (could just be due to length & multi-modal approach)
	Participation not voluntary, could affect results
	May be more effective with some types of antisocial behaviour than others
Mixed results for more serious cases/not evaluated	
Functional family therapy	Only tested on small samples involving less severe cases
Cognitive-behavioural therapy	Success reported with juvenile offenders. However, short-term nature of programmes means may be unsuitable for seriousness of behaviour developing into ASPD
Multi-modal programmes	Few evaluations on effectiveness
	Mixed results where evaluations exist
Psychotherapy	Not good for resistant & poorly motivated clients
	Not suitable as primary means of treatment

Therapeutic communities	Few evaluations for use with adolescents Regimes vary considerably, but under certain conditions, certain clients might benefit. Needs more testing
Parent training	Less effective with adolescents and with more severely disturbed children
Unlikely to help ASPD Broad preventative programmes	Fail to reach most difficult & disturbed individuals

Generally, multi-modal interventions that are well organised and structured, and those that are intensive in nature may prove more effective in the long run, although initially more costly. It is also likely that lengthy or repeated interventions are required to sustain improved functioning in those at the highest risk. Different interventions may be required at different stages in an individual's development, with regular booster sessions across the life course, since few interventions offer really long-term benefit. It is also important to consider severely antisocial adolescents as a heterogeneous group, since evidence suggests that it may be possible to match treatment type to characteristics of the client.

Whatever the nature of the intervention offered, it is generally agreed that it needs to be theory-based, addressing known causal factors in the development of personality disorder. Unfortunately, theory is not well developed enough to allow us to be prescriptive about the content of interventions for this group. However, we do know that it should emphasise pro-social behaviour and potentially protective factors, building on the young person's strengths as well as tackling antisocial behaviour and antecedent risk factors. Regardless of the treatment setting, the intervention should be carried out in a manner consistent with its original design, since treatment integrity can affect results. The intervention should also address co-morbid conditions such as substance abuse and depression, which are frequent in this group, and may aggravate behavioural problems. These features have yet to be incorporated into an evaluation study without methodological flaws. Until then, we cannot give a definitive answer to the question of what works.

7   Conclusions and policy implications

Introduction

If, as Dolan (1998) comments, 'our knowledge of effective treatments for personality disorders remains rudimentary', then our knowledge of effective interventions with high-risk adolescents to prevent development of personality disorders is crude indeed. The need to establish guidelines for the identification and treatment of this group is an increasingly significant issue, given that rates of psychosocial disorders are likely to increase in coming decades (Rutter & Smith, 1995). This final section of the report draws together conclusions from the literature, and spells out implications for policy, practice and research.

Main conclusions

The present report has largely dealt with antisocial behaviour in adolescence and its potential trajectory into adult ASPD, which affects a relatively small number of individuals. Some individuals diagnosed as ASPD may also be described as DSPD (the latter not constituting a clear diagnostic category in the same manner as the former), on the grounds that they may pose a substantial risk to the public, and for this reason are currently a concern for government. A review of the evidence suggests that we have limited knowledge of the risk factors that lead to ASPD, and an even more limited knowledge of the best means of identifying high-risk adolescents on a trajectory into ASPD. Research evaluating interventions with high-risk adolescents suggests that most promise lies in the use of intensive, structured, multi-modal programmes.

Implications for policy and practice

The main obstacle for policy makers and practitioners in this area is the lack of informative studies that can be drawn on to inform decision-making. Since most intervention studies tackle antisocial behaviour of less severity, caution is required when generalising to prevention of dangerous and severe personality disorders. Of the interventions reviewed in this report, it is clear that there is no 'quick fix' for identifying or intervening with high-risk adolescents. Identification of a core group with the worst prognosis remains a significant problem with important cost implications. Whichever approach to intervention is the preferred route, it is likely to be intensive, repeated, and costly if long-term benefits are to be derived. However, there are no definitive studies that point the way forward for devising policy to assert when, with whom, and how often intervention should take place in order to prevent ASPD.

Service provision

Interventions happen within the broader context of existing services, particularly for the most extreme groups. Despite investment in interventions targeted at vulnerable individuals early in life, 'there will always be a group who fall through the net and challenge our abilities to offer suitable care and treatment' (Maher, Kelly, & Cook, 2000). The needs of this group are so varied, complex and difficult to meet that they are unlikely to be resolved by a single resource or intervention provided by health or social services, education departments or the youth justice service. Multi-disciplinary working is essential. To work effectively in a multi-disciplinary context, Maher and others (2000) suggest that different world-views, different languages and issues of authority, ownership, control and responsibility must be resolved. A number of recommendations have been put forward to maximise the effectiveness of multi-disciplinary working within services:

- an agreed joint statement of aims and objective
- a clearly understood and effective managerial structure
- a central base that promotes cohesion and continuity in multi-disciplinary working
- competent professional practice underpinned by training and supervision, clear referral practices and procedures, and management of time and resources
- co-operative rather than competitive working relationships
- monitoring and supervision via regular focused meetings
- the appointment of a professional to act as co-ordinator and convenor
- acknowledging and tackling issues of leadership and other tensions arising from multi-disciplinary work
- providing clarity about whether a multi-disciplinary team is dealing with a case or else a network of professionals
- designation of responsibility for cases to specific key workers so that all elements of the service are clear as to responsibility they hold.

(NHS/Health Advisory Service, 1995)

There are several ways in which such interdisciplinary services can be structured and funded. An example is provided by Maher and colleagues in Surrey, who are consulting with representatives from health, social services and education departments to consider provision of a highly specialised service for adolescents with 'complex needs'. They describe current provision for such adolescents as 'separate, ad-hoc and often crisis-driven' (p 11; Maher et al, 2000), and suggest the development of a new multi-agency service, in line with national initiatives such as 'Quality Protects' and 'Partnerships in Action'. The proposed new service, based on one site, would involve a day care and support provision and possibly a small residential unit. Whichever approach is adopted for the provision of services, a 'coherent and holistic programme' (Mental Health Foundation, 1999) is needed to stem the tide of mental health problems of young people, which are likely to grow in complexity and severity if present trends continue.

Staff training

Working with such difficult, treatment-resistant adolescents is likely to be demanding and demoralising, and may adversely affect staff attitudes to clients. A recent study amongst nursing staff in three high security hospitals who work with adult personality disordered patients showed that three out of four nurses felt inadequately prepared for working with this group, and that fewer than one in five nurses expressed any optimism about treatment of such patients, who some perceived as 'evil' (Bowers, 2000).

McGuire (1995) stresses the need for staff to combine sensitivity and constructiveness in relating to clients, and suggests that their competing roles of 'law-enforcement' and 'social work' need not be incompatible. Evidence also suggests that staff need to carry out programmes in a way that does not compromise the integrity of the intervention as it was originally envisaged, since this has a detrimental impact on programme effectiveness. This means raising staff awareness of the importance of programme integrity, and establishing a means of monitoring it and preserving it. However, to achieve this approach, staff training and supervision are required. McGuire (1995) suggests that current staff training, both professional and in-service training, needs to be modified to take account of these issues. In addition, many of the interventions reviewed in the preceding chapter, such as multisystemic treatment and functional family therapy, require specialist training, supervision and support of staff. These are likely to be costly, but such costs must be balanced against the costs of long-term treatment or incarceration of personality disordered adults. There is still much that is not known about what constitutes good practice for selection, training and supervision of staff to work with this high-risk group.

Directions for future research

Research in the area of APSD is likely to involve studies that are lengthy and therefore slow in providing resolutions to the pressing need to find interventions that work in reducing risk. It is important therefore to identify areas that should be prioritised amongst the many that need further investigation. Assigning priorities to this research agenda will be in part determined by the professional perspective from which the subject area is approached. The concerns of epidemiologists, for example, may be very different to the concerns of policy advisors, clinical psychologists, or members of Youth Offending Teams. One way of viewing these research priorities is in terms of 'pure' research areas (such as aetiological investigation) and 'applied' areas (such as treatment effectiveness), although in reality there is much common ground between them, since one is required to inform the other.

Formulating a research agenda in the general area of adolescent forensic psychiatry is a task that is currently being undertaken by a team led by Dr Susan Bailey at Salford Adolescent Forensic Services in Manchester, under instruction from the NHS Executive as part of the National Programme on Forensic Mental Health Research and Development. In addition, the joint Home Office, Department of Health and Prison Service programme on Dangerousness and Severe personality Disorder has established a major programme of research on the assessment, treatment and prevention of DSPD.

A primary issue that we have referred to on several occasions in the body of this report is the problem of terminology, diagnosis and classification. Terms are used as if of equal discriminatory power, when in fact some terms are parts of internationally agreed diagnostic criteria, whereas others are simply phrases that have been used in various contexts but which have never been clearly defined. In addition, studies in this area (and different disciplines) focus on different sub-groups and it is hard to compare like with like. In order to capitalise on research, there needs to be more systematising of definitions, and more general agreement about how groups are delineated.

These issues are related, of course, to problems of measurement and accurate identification – a definition is meaningless if it cannot be operationalised. Examples of research needs in this area relate to development of assessment scales for use by professionals from different backgrounds but meeting similar clients (social workers, police, and nurses, for example). It is clear that issues of measurement or identification are not purely 'academic' – there are very clear practical and service implications, in the need to develop methods of assessment to identify level of client risk, and also to identify clients' needs. Both are required to facilitate client selection and allocation to different types of interventions. Thus research is needed to compare the effectiveness of different risk assessment tools, and tools assessing criminological needs. Such research could be conducted on a wide scale, involving a number of judicial agencies, so that data could be combined from different settings.

Once terms and diagnoses are more transparent and comparable, and measurement more accurate, research on patterns and trends is a second priority area. There are significant gaps in our understanding of frequencies and rates of disorders in different populations, representative and selected. For example, understanding prevalence of ASPD in groups of young people receiving different kinds of services would be a useful addition to our existing knowledge of prevalence among adults in prisons etc.

Third, in addition to issues of measurement and epidemiology, there is a need to uncover more about the aetiological pathways involved in ASPD. Further research in this area will assist with the identification of high-risk individuals, since developing an instrument for early identification presupposes a knowledge of pertinent risk factors. Such research will also pinpoint the risk and protective factors that interventions should address. Given that early-onset conduct problems and co-morbid ADHD appear to be significant risk factors, long-term follow-up of a group of children with such characteristics would be one potential area of investigation. This would enable us to be more precise about the additional risk factors that contribute to ASPD and their mode of operation. It may then be possible to delineate more clearly the features of sub-groups (e.g. those with cold and callous traits) that are most likely to develop into adult psychopaths. Since this is necessarily a lengthy process, an accelerated cohort study could be used, in which selected children of different ages are followed up to explore the continuities and discontinuities in risk and protective factors from birth to adulthood. To maximise the ability of the study to untangle sequencing of relevant causal factors, the use of intensive investigator-based interviewing is preferable in addition to self-report questionnaire methods. However, even within a series of children with early-onset conduct disorder and ADHD, only a small number are likely to develop ASPD. This necessitates sample sizes adequate to detect significant effects. Such children and families may also be difficult to recruit and retain in a long-term research study, especially if parents themselves have ASPD, which is likely in some cases. Studies might:

- specifically address severe personality disorder as an outcome rather than broader topics such as antisocial behaviour or offending
- use a variety of designs, including retrospective designs of high risk groups, which are useful in identifying likely risk factors; longitudinal designs with regular follow-ups, assessing a range of factors and tracking changes and patterns of interaction of factors over time; and experimental designs that test how altering a factor can influence an outcome

- include females as well as males to identify differences in developmental pathways as well as treatment effectiveness
- assess protective factors as well as risk factors, as these may have significance for the design of interventions
- identify the specific factor or cluster of factors that relate to ASPD rather than other disorders
- go beyond the mere identification of a risk factor to isolate the mechanism by which the factor works
- develop a stronger theoretical base in order to devise interventions that tackle causal mechanisms involved in development of personality disorder.

Fourth, there is a need for scientifically rigorous evaluation of existing interventions, particularly those with features most associated with promising outcomes. These include programmes that are multi-modal, intensive, well structured, and lengthy. Of the interventions reviewed in this report, multisystemic treatment, functional family therapy, treatment foster care, multi-modal cognitive-behavioural packages, and some therapeutic communities share these features, and offer some hope for improving outcome. Well-designed studies are now needed to evaluate the effectiveness of these programmes, and need to be carried out in line with the methodological recommendations outlined in Chapter 4. However, even if some interventions produce promising results, it is important to acknowledge that there will always be a treatment-resistant group who will potentially require therapeutic support and case management for most of their lives. Detailed assessment of characteristics of individuals at the outset of an intervention may help to identify the features of those who are most likely to respond to treatment. In addition, amongst individuals who do respond, continued intervention and support may also be required, though of a less intensive nature. In research terms therefore, it is preferable to carry out a relatively long-term follow-up of a treatment series to detect the stage at which additional intervention is required, and to assess the effects of additional 'top-up' interventions. Studies addressing this priority area might:

- devise and test methods of identification and assessment of adolescents who should be targeted for more intensive interventions. This may only be possible when more is known about the particular cluster of risk factors of significance in the development of ASPD
- involve a number of settings for testing interventions including criminal justice and custodial settings as well as health care settings
- identify more closely the characteristics of treatment and client that optimise success

- include cost-benefits analysis, calculated on a basis that is common across studies
- replicate successful interventions so that policy can be formulated on the basis of reliable research findings.

Evaluation of multisystemic therapy, treatment foster care and functional family therapy have not taken place in the UK to our knowledge. Results from abroad are encouraging, and these interventions would seem to represent a potentially useful way forward. This would entail training individuals in these specialist methods, and setting up evaluations of these programmes in a number of settings.

In terms of interventions currently available in the UK, therapeutic communities for adolescents have been running for some time, but rigorous evaluations of them have not taken place, and are now needed. There have also been a number of cognitive-behavioural therapy programmes running for young offenders, some of which are now being evaluated. Such evaluations should continue, and results should be disseminated to practitioners and managers. If a sufficient number of such evaluations are conducted and carried out with sufficient scientific rigour, then we may be able to draw up guidelines as to (1) the suitability of clients for certain interventions, given the level of client risk and need, (2) requirements for staff training and supervision, and (3) the best way to implement interventions in a number of different settings, given the sorts of difficulties described earlier in areas such as multi-disciplinary working.

Conclusions

As this review shows, there are significant gaps in our knowledge concerning interventions that work for adolescents in preventing severe antisocial personality disorder. The formation of policy in this area may be substantially hindered as a result. Tolan and Gorman-Smith (1997) pessimistically conclude that 'the current scientific knowledge base about risk is too limited in power and accuracy to justify legally based action or to specify which intervention programmes should be provided to which youths' (p 410). They suggest that 'the present scientific knowledge can guide but not fully direct' (Tolan & Gorman-Smith, 1997). On a more optimistic note, this review found some support, though often weak, for the effectiveness of some interventions with some individuals. It appears that prevention of ASPD is likely to be an endeavour stretching from infancy to adulthood in the lives of those at risk. However, until further research is forthcoming, the questions of whom to intervene with and how remain uncertain. Much more research needs to be undertaken to establish conclusive evidence of the power of interventions to alter the trajectory of very high-risk groups.

Alexander, J.F. & Parsons, B.V. (1973) Short-term behavioural intervention with delinquent families: Impact on family process and recidivism. *Journal of Abnormal Psychology*, 81, 219-225.

Alexander, J.F. & Parsons, B.V. (1982) *Functional family therapy*. Monterey, CA: Brooks/Cole.

Allen, J.P. & Land, D. (1999) Attachment in adolescence. In J. Cassidy & P.R. Shaver (Eds). *Handbook of attachment: Theory, research and clinical applications*, 319-335. New York: Guilford Press.

American Psychiatric Association (1994) *Diagnostic and statistical manual of mental disorders* (4th edition) (DSM-IV). Washington, DC: American Psychiatric Association.

Andrews, D.A. (1995) The psychology of criminal conduct and effective treatment. In J. McGuire (Ed.), *What works: Reducing reoffending. Guidelines from research and practice*, 35-62. Chichester: John Wiley and Sons.

Andrews, D.A., Zinger, I., Hoge, R.D., Bonta, J. et al (1996) In D.F. Greenberg (Ed.), *Criminal Careers, Volume 2. The International library of criminology, criminal justice and penology*, 437-472. England: Dartmouth Publishing Company Limited.

Audit Commission (1996) *Misspent Youth: Young people and crime*. Abingdon: Audit Commission Publications.

Augimeri, L.K., Webster, C.D., Koegl, C.J., and Levene, K.S. (1998) *Early Assessment Risk List for Boys (Version 1): Consultation Edition*. Toronto, Ontario: Earlscourt Child and Family Centre.

Bailey, S. (1996) Adolescents who murder. *Journal of Adolescence*, 19, 19-39.

Bank, L., Marlowe, J.H., Reid, J.B., Patterson, G.R., & Weinrott, M.R. (1991) A comparative evaluation of parent-training interventions for families of chronic delinquents. *Journal of Abnormal Child Psychology*, 19, 15-33.

Barry, K.L., Fleming, M.F., Manwell, L.B., & Copeland, L.A. (1997) Conduct disorder and antisocial personality in adult primary care patients. *Journal of Family Practice, 45*(2), 151-158.

Barton, C., Alexander, J.F., Waldron, H., Turner, C.W., & Warburton, J. (1985) Generalising treatment effects of Functional Family Therapy: Three replications. *American Journal of Family Therapy, 13,* 16-26.

Baruch, G. (2000) *A randomised controlled trial testing psychologically based interventions for young offenders.* (Manuscript in preparation).

Beck, A.T., Freeman, A., Pretzer, J., Davis, D.D., Fleming, B., Ottaviani, R., Beck, J., Simon, K.M., Padesky, C., Meyer, J., & Trexler, L. (1990) *Cognitive therapy of personality disorders.* New York: Guilford Press.

Bifulco, A., & Moran, P. (1998) *Wednesday's child. Research into women's experience of neglect and abuse in childhood, and adult depression.* London: Routledge.

Black, D.W., Monahan, P., Baumgard, C.H., & Bell, S.E. (1997) Predictors of long-term outcome in 45 men with antisocial personality disorder. *Annals of Clinical Psychiatry, 9*(4), 211-217.

Blackburn, R. (1993) Clinical programmes with psychopaths. In K. Howells & C. Hollis (Eds.), *Clinical Approaches to the Mentally Disordered Offender.* Chichester: Wiley.

Blackburn, R. (2000) Treatment or incapacitation? Implications of research on personality disorders for the management of dangerous offenders. *Legal and Criminological Psychology, 5,* 1-21.

Blackburn, R. & Coid, J.W. (1999) Empirical clusters of DSM-III personality disorders in violent offenders. *Journal of Personality Disorders, 13,* 18-34.

Bland, R.C., Newman, S.C., & Orn, H. (1987) Schizophrenia: Lifetime co-morbidity in a community sample. *Acta Psychiatrica Scandinavica, 75*(4), 383-391.

Bland, R.C., Orn, H., & Newman, S.C. (1988) Lifetime prevalence of psychiatric disorders in Edmonton. *Acta Psychiatrica Scandinavica, 77* (suppl. 338), 24-32.

Bland, R.C., Stebelsky, G., Orn, H., & Newman, S.C. (1988) Psychiatric disorders and unemployment in Edmonton. *Acta Psychiatrica Scandinavica, 77* (suppl. 338), 72-80.

Bonta, J., Law, M., and Hanson, R.K. (1998) The prediction of criminal and violent recidivism among mentally disordered offenders: A meta-analysis. *Psychological Bulletin*, 123, 123-142.

Borduin, C.M., Mann, B.J., Cone, L.T., Henggeler, S.W., Fucci, B.R., Blaske, D.M., & Williams, R.A. (1995) Multisystemic treatment of serious juvenile offenders: Long-term prevention of criminality and violence. *Journal of Consulting and Clinical Psychology*, 63, 569-578.

Bowers, L. (2000) *Misunderstood misfits or psychological vampires: Psychiatric nurse attitudes to personality disordered patients.* Presentation at Research and Development Seminar: Cross-government research and development for mentally disordered offenders, policy and service development.

BPS (1999) *Dangerous people with severe personality disorder. A British Psychological Society Response.*

Brewer, D.D., Hawkins, J.D., Catalano, R.F., & Neckerman, J.J. (1995) Preventing serious, violent and chronic juvenile offending: A review of evaluations of selected strategies in childhood, adolescence, and the community. In J.C. Howell, B. Krisberg, J.D. Hawkins, & J.J. Wilson, (Eds.), *Serious, violent, and chronic juvenile offenders*, 61-141. London: Sage Publications Ltd.

Bronfenbrenner, U. (1979) *The ecology of human development.* Cambridge, MA: Harvard University Press.

Brunck, M. (1999) *Effective treatment of conduct disorder.* Internet publication at : http:/www.ilppp.virginia.edu/juv/ConDis.html.

Bullock, R., Little, M., & Millham, S. (1998) *Secure treatment outcomes. The care careers of very different adolescents.* Aldershot: Ashgate.

Cadoret, R.J., Yates, W.R., Troughton, E., Woodworth, G., & Stewart, M.A. (1995) Genetic-environmental interaction in the genesis of aggressivity and conduct disorders. *Archives of General Psychiatry*, 52, 916-924.

Capaldi, D.M., & Stoolmiller, M. (1999) Co-occurrence of conduct problems and depressive symptoms in early adolescent boys: III. Prediction to young-adult adjustment. *Development and Psychopathology*, 11, 59-84.

Capara, G.V., & Rutter, M. (1995) Individual development and social change: Some concepts and issues. In M. Rutter, & D. Smith, (Eds.), *Psychosocial disorders in young people: Time trends and their origins.* Chichester: Wiley.

Caspi, A., Henry, B., McGee, R.O., Moffitt, T.E., & Silva, P.A. (1995) Temperamental origins of child and adolescent behaviour problems: From age 3 to age 15. *Child Development*, 66, 55-68.

Caspi, A., & Moffitt, T.E. (1995) The continuity of maladaptive behaviour: From description to understanding in the study of antisocial behaviour. In D. Chicchetti, & D. Cohen, (Eds.), *Developmental psychopathology: Volume 2. Risk, disorder and adaptation*, 472-511. New York: Wiley.

Chamberlain, P. (1994) *Family Connections.* Eugene, OR: Castalia.

Chamberlain, P., & Moore, K. J. (1998) Models of community treatment for serious juvenile offenders. In J. Crane, (Ed.), *Social programmes that really work.* New York: Russell Sage Foundation.

Chamberlain, P., & Reid, J. B. (1994) Differences in risk factors and adjustment for male and female delinquents in treatment foster care. *Journal of Child and Family Studies*, 3, 23-39.

Chilcoat, H.D., & Anthony, J.C. (1996) Impact of parent monitoring on initiation of drug use through late childhood. *Journal of the American Academy of Child and Adolescent Psychiatry*, 35, 91-100.

Christian, R.E., Frick, P.J., Hill, N.L, Tyler, A.L., & Frazer, D.R (1997) Psychopathy and conduct problems in children: II. Implications for subtyping children with conduct problems. *Journal of the American Academy of Child and Adolescent Psychiatry*, 36, 233-41.

Cleckley, H. (1941) *The mask of sanity.* St Louis, MO: C.V. Mosby Co.

Cohen, P., Cohen, J., Kasen, S., Velez, C.N., Hartmark, C., Johnson, J., Rojas, M., Brook, J., & Streuning, E.L. (1993) An epidemiological study of disorders in late childhood and adolescence: I. Age and gender-specific prevalence. *Journal of Child Psychology and Psychiatry*, 34, 851-67.

Cohen, H., & Filipczak, J. (1971) *A new learning environment.* San Francisco: Jossey-Bass.

Coid, J.W. (1992) DSM-III diagnosis in criminal psychopaths: A way forward. *Criminal Behaviour and Mental Health,* 2, 78-79.

Coid, J.W. (1998) The management of dangerous psychopaths in prison. In T. Millon, E. Simonsen, M. Birket-Smith, & R.D. Davis, (Eds.), *Psychopathy, antisocial, criminal and violent behaviour,* 407-430. New York/London :The Guildford Press.

Coid, J.W. (1999) *Aetiological risk factors for personality disorders.* British Journal of Psychiatry, 174, 530-538.

Coie, J.D., Terry, R., Zakriski, A., & Lochman, J.E. (1995) *Early adolescent social influences on delinquent behaviour.* In J. McCord (Ed.), Coercion and punishment in long-term perspectives, 229-244. New York: Cambridge University Press.

Coleman, J. (1999) *Key data on adolescence.* Brighton: Trust for the Study of Adolescence.

Coleman, J. & Hendry, L. (1999) T*he nature of adolescence.* 2nd Edition. London: Routledge.

Coleman, J., Henricson, C., & Roker, D. (1999) *Parenting in the youth justice context.* Internet publication at: http:/www.tsa.uk.com.

Collins, J.J., Schlenger, W.E., & Jordan, B.K. (1988) Antisocial personality and substance abuse disorders. *Bulletin of the American Academy of Psychiatry and the Law,* 16(2), 187-198.

Conger, R.D., Patterson, G.R., & Ge, X. (1995) It takes two to replicate: A mediational model for the impact of parents' stress on adolescent adjustment. *Child Development, 66,* 80-97.

Cooke, D.J. (1989) Containing violent prisoners: An analysis of Barlinnie special unit. *British Journal of Criminology,* 129, 129-143.

Craft, M., Stephenson, G., & Granger, C. (1964) A controlled trial of authoritarian and self-governing regimes with adolescent psychopaths. *American Journal of Orthopsychiatry, 64,* 543-554.

Daniel, A.E., Harris, P.W., & Husain, S.A. (1981) Differences between midlife female offenders and those younger than 40. *American Journal of Psychiatry,* 138:9, 1225-1228.

Daniel, A.E., Parraga, H., Beeks, E.C., & Belsky, D. (1983) Psychiatric diagnosis and pattern of drug abuse among violent adolescent criminals. *American Journal of Forensic Psychiatry*, 4(1), 5-20.

Deckel, A.W., Hesselbrock, V., & Bauer, L. (1996) *Antisocial personality disorder, childhood delinquency, and frontal brain functioning: EEG and neuropsychological findings.* Journal of Clinical Psychology, 52, 639-650.

DiLalla, L.F., & Gottesman, I.I. (1989) Heterogeneity of causes for delinquency and criminality: Lifespan perspectives. *Development and Psychopathology*, 1, 339-349.

Dodge, K.A. (1980) Social cognition and children's aggressive behaviour. *Child Development*, 51, 162-170.

Dodge, K.A. (1986) A social information processing model of social competence in children. In M. Perlmutter (Ed.), *The Minnesota symposium on child psychology*, 18, 17-125. Hillsdale, NJ: Erlbaum.

Dodge, K.A., Pettitt, G.S., Bates, J.E., & Valente, E. (1995) Social information-processing patterns partially mediate the effect of early physical abuse on later conduct problems. *Journal of Abnormal Psychology*, 104, 632-643.

Dodge, K.A., & Schwartz, D. (1997) Social information processing mechanisms in aggressive behaviour. In D. Stoff, J. Breiling, & J.D. Maser (Eds.), *Handbook of Antisocial Behaviour*, 171-80. New York: Wiley.

Dolan, B. (1998) Therapeutic community treatment for severe personality disorders. In T. Millon, E. Simonsen, M. Birket-Smith, & R.D. Davis, (Eds.), *Psychopathy, antisocial, criminal and violent behaviour*, 407-430. New York/London :The Guildford Press.

Dolan, B., & Coid, J. (1993) *Psychopathic and Antisocial Personality Disorders*. London: Gaskell.

Douglas, K.S., Cox, D.N., and Webster, C.D. (1999) Violence risk assessment: Science and practice. *Legal and Criminal Psychology*, 4, 149-184.

Dyck, R.J., Bland, R.C., Newman, S.C., & Orn, H. (1988) Suicide attempts and psychiatric disorders in Edmonton. *Acta Psychiatrica Scandinavica*, 77 (suppl. 338), 64-71.

Erikson, E.H. (1968) *Identity, youth and crisis*. New York: Norton.

Farrington, D.P. (1991) Childhood aggression and adult violence. In D. Pepler & K.H. Rubin (Eds.), *The development and treatment of childhood aggression*, 5-29. Hillsdale, NJ: Erlbaum.

Farrington, D.P. (1995) The twelfth Jack Tizard Memorial Lecture. The development of offending and antisocial behaviour from childhood: Key findings from the Cambridge Study in Delinquent Development, *Journal of Child Psychology and Psychiatry*, 36(6), 929-964.

Farrington, D.P. (1999) The psychosocial milieu of the offender. In J. Gunn, & P.J. Taylor (Eds.), *Forensic Psychiatry: Clinical , Legal and Ethical Issues*, 252-285. Oxford: Butterman-Heinemann.

Farrington, D.P., Gallagher, B., Morley, L., St. Ledger, R.J., & West, D.J. (1986) Unemployment, school leaving and crime. *British Journal of Criminology*, 26 335-356.

Farrington, D.P., & West, D.J. (1990) The Cambridge study in delinquent development: A long-term follow-up of 411 London males. In H-J. Kerner, & G. Kaiser (Eds.), *Kriminalitat: Personlichkeit, lebensgeschichte und verhalten (Criminality: Personality, behaviour and life history)*, 115-138. Berlin: Springer-Verlag.

Farrington, D.P., & West, D.J. (1995) Effects of marriage, separation and children on offending by adult males. In Z.S. Blau, & J Hagen (Eds.), *Current perspectives on ageing and the life cycle. Delinquency and disrepute in the life course*, 4, 249-281. Greenwich, CT: JAI Press.

Fauber, R., Forehand, R., Thomas, A.M., & Wierson, M. (1990) *A mediational model of the impact of marital conflict on adolescent adjustment in intact and divorced families: The role of disrupted parenting*. Child Development, 61, 1112-1123.

Fitzgerald, J. (1990). *The hurt and the healing: A study of therapeutic communities for children and young people comprising the Charterhouse Group*. London: The Charterhouse Group.

Fonagy, P. et al. (2000) *What works for which child*. A report commissioned by the National Health Service Executive. (Manuscript in preparation).

Forth, A.E., Hart, S.D. and Hare, R.D. (1990) Assessment of psychopathy in male young offenders. *Psychological Assessment: A Journal of Consulting and Clinical Psychology*, 2, 342-344.

Forth, A.E., Kosson, D. and Hare, R.D. (in press) *The Hare Psychopathy Checklist: Youth Version.* Toronto, Canada: Multi-Health Systems.

Freud, A. (1958) Adolescence. *Psychoanalytic Study of the Child,* 13, 255-278.

Frick, P.J. (1996) Callous-unemotional traits and conduct problems: A two-factor model of psychopathy in children. In D.J. Cooke, A.E. Forth, J.P. Newman, & R.D. Hare (Eds.), *International perspectives on psychopathy. Issues in criminological and legal psychology,* No. 24, 47-51. Leicester: British Psychological Society.

Frick, P.J., Christian, R.E., Wooton, J.M. (1999) Age trends in association between parenting practices and conduct problems. *Behaviour Modification,* 23(1), 106-128.

Frick, P.J., O'Brien, B.S., Wootton, J.M., & McBurnett, K. (1994) Psychopathy and conduct problems in children. *Journal of Abnormal Psychology,* 103(4), 700-707.

Furnham, A., & Gunter, B. (1989) *Young people's social attitude in Britain: The anatomy of adolescence.* London: Routledge.

Garmezy, N. (1981) Personality development. In A.J. Robin, A.M. Aronoff, R.A. Barclay, et al (Eds.), *Further explorations in personality,* 196-269. New York: Wiley.

Garrett, P (1985) Effects of residential treatment of adjudicated delinquents: A meta-analysis. *Journal of Research in Crime and Delinquency,* 22, 287-308.

Garrido, V., Esteban, C., & Molero, C. (1996). The effectiveness in the treatment of psychopaths: A meta-analysis. In D.J. Cooke, A.E. Forth, J. Newman & R.D. Hare (Eds.), *International perspectives on psychopathy. Issues in criminological and legal psychology,* No. 24, 94-99. Leicester: British Psychological Society.

Garvey, M.J., & Spoden, F. (1980) Suicide attempts in antisocial personality disorder. *Comprehensive Psychiatry,* 21(2), 146-149.

Goldstein, A.P., & Glick, B. (1994) Aggressive replacement training: Curriculum and evaluation. *Simulation and Gaming,* 25, 9-26.

Goldstein, R.B., Powers, S.I., McCusker, J., & Mundt, K.A. (1996) Gender differences in manifestations of antisocial personality disorder among residential drug abuse treatment clients. *Drug and Alcohol Dependence,* 41(1), 35-45.

Goodman, R. (1994) Brain development. In M. Rutter, & D.F. Hay (Eds.), *Development through life: A handbook for clinicians*, 49-78. Oxford: Blackwell Scientific Publications.

Gordon, D.A., Graves, K., & Arbuthnot, J. (1995) The effect of functional family therapy for delinquents on adult criminal behaviour. *Criminal Justice and Behaviour*, 22, 60-73.

Graham, J., & Bowling, B. (1995) *Young people and crime*. (Home Office Research Study No. 145). London: HMSO.

Greenberg, M.T., Speltz, M.L. & DeKlyen, M. (1993) The role of attachment in the early development of disruptive behaviour problems. *Development and Psychopathology*, 5, 191-213.

Greenman, D.A., Gunderson, J.G., Cane, M. et al. (1986) An examination of the borderline diagnosis in children. *American Journal of Psychiatry*, 143, 998-1003.

Gretton, H.M., McBride, H.L., O'Shaughnessy, R., & Hare, R.D. (1997) *Sex offender or generalized offender?: Psychopathy as a risk marker for violence in adolescent offenders*. Paper presented at the 5th International Congress on the Disorders of Personality, Vancouver, British Columbia.

Guerra, N., & Slaby, R.G. (1990) Cognitive mediators of aggression in adolescent offenders: 11. Intervention. *Developmental Psychology*, 26, 269-277.

Gunn, J. & Robertson, G.R. (1982). An evaluation of Grendon Prison. In J. Gunn, & D.P. Farrington (Eds.), *Abnormal offenders, delinquency, and the criminal justice system*, 285-305. New York: Wiley.

Hall, G.S. (1904) *Adolescence: Its psychology and its relations to physiology, anthropology, sociology, sex, crime, religion and education* (Vols. 1 & 2). New York: Appleton.

Hämäläinen, M., & Pulkkinen, L. (1995) Aggressive and non-prosocial behaviour as precursors of criminality. *Studies on crime and crime prevention*, 4, 6-20.

Hare, R.D. (1970) *Psychopathy: Theory and research*. New York: Wiley.

Hare, R.D. (1985) A comparison of procedures for the assessment of psychopathy. *Journal of Consulting and Clinical Psychology*, 53, 7-16.

Hare, R.D. (1991) *The Hare Psychopathy Checklist – Revised.* Toronto: Multi-Health Systems.

Hare, R.D. (1998) Psychopathy, affect, and behaviour. In D.J. Cooke, A.E. Forth, & R.D. Hare (Eds.), *Psychopathy: Theory, research, and implications for society,* 105-138. Dordrecht, The Netherlands: Kluwer.

Hare, R.D., & McPherson, I.M. (1984) Violent and aggressive behaviour in criminal psychopaths. *International Journal of Law and Psychiatry, 7,* 35-50.

Harpur, T.J., & Hare, R.D. (1994) Assessment of psychopathy as a function of age. *Journal of Abnormal Psychology,* 103(4), 604-609.

Harris, G.T., Rice, M.E. & Cormier, C.A. (1994) Psychopaths: Is a therapeutic community therapeutic? *Therapeutic Communities,* 15(4), 283-299.

Hart, S.D., & Hare, R.D. (1997) Psychopathy: Assessment and association with criminal conduct. In D.M. Stoff, J. Breiling, & J.D. Maser (Eds.), *Handbook of Antisocial Behaviour,* 22-35. Chichester: Wiley.

Hay, D.F., Castle, J., & Jewett, J. (1994) Character development. In M. Rutter, & D. Hay (Eds.), *Development through life: A handbook for clinicians,* 319-349. Oxford: Blackwell Science Ltd.

Hemphill, J.F., Hare, R.D., and Wong, S. (1998) Psychopathy and recidivism: A review. *Legal and Criminal Psychology, 3,* 139-170.

Henggeler, S.W., & Borduin, C.M. (1990) *Family therapy and beyond: A multisystemic approach to treating the behaviour problems of children and adolescents.* Pacific Grove, CA: Brooks/Cole.

Henggeler, S.W., Melton, G.B., Smith, L.A., Schoenwald, S.K., & Hanley, J.H. (1993) Family preservation using multisystemic treatment: Long-term follow-up to a clinical trial with serious juvenile offenders. *Journal of Child and Family Studies, 2,* 283-293.

Henggeler, S.W., Melton, G.B., Brondino, M.J., Scherer, D.G., & Hanley, J.H. (1997) Multisystemic Therapy with violent and chronic juvenile offenders and their families: The role of treatment fidelity in successful dissemination. *Journal of Consulting and Clinical Psychology,* 65, 821-833.

Henggeler, S.W., Schoenwald, S.K., Borduin, C.M., Rowland, M.D., & Cunningham, P. B. (1998) *Multisystemic treatment for antisocial behaviour in children and adolescents*. New York: Guilford Press.

Herman, J.L. (1992) *Trauma and recovery from domestic abuse to political terror*. New York: Basic Books.

Hill, J. & Rutter, M. (1994) Personality disorders. In M., Rutter, E. Taylor, & I. Hersov,. *Child and Adolescent Services: Modern Approaches*. Oxford: Blackwell Scientific Publications.

Hirschi, T. & Hindelang, M.T. (1977) *Intelligence and delinquency: A revisionist reivew*. American Social Review, 42, 571-87.

Hoffart, A., Thornes, K., & Hedley, L.M et al (1994) DSM III-R Axis I and II disorders in agoraphobic patients with and without panic disorder. *Acta Psychiatrica Scandinavica, 89*, 186-191.

Holdcraft, L.C., Iacono, W.G., & McGue, M.K. (1998) Antisocial personality disorder and depression in relation to alcoholism: A community-based sample. *Journal of Studies on Alcohol, 59*(2), 222-226.

Hollin, C. (1995) *Working with offenders*. Chichester: John Wiley & Sons.

Home Office (1997) *Young prisoners: Thematic review by HM Chief Inspector of prisons for England and Wales*. Internet publication at: http://www.homeoffice.gov.uk/hmipris/yprispref.htm.

Home Office (1998) *Criminal Statistics England and Wales 1997* . London: The Stationery Office.

Home Office/Department of Health (1999) *Managing dangerous people with severe personality disorder*. London: Department of Health.

Home Office/Department of Health (1999) *Reforming the Mental Health Act*. London: Stationary Office.

Howell, J.C., Krisberg, B., Hawkins, J.D., & Wilson, J.J. (Eds.) (1995) *Serious, violent, and chronic juvenile offenders*. London: Sage Publications Ltd.

Johnson, J.G., Cohen, P., Brown, J., Smailes, E., and Berstein, D.P. (1999) Childhood maltreatment increases risk for personality disorders during early adulthood. *Archives of General Psychiatry,* 56, 600-606.

Kasen, S., Cohen, P., Skodol, A.E., Johnson, J.G. & Brook, J.S. (1999) Influence of child and adolescent psychiatric disorders on young adult personality disorder. *American Journal of Psychiatry,* 156, 1529-1535.

Kazdin, A.E. (1995) Child, parent, and family dysfunction as predictors of outcome in cognitive-behavioural treatment of antisocial children. *Behavioural Research and Therapy,* 33, 271-281.

Kazdin, A. (1996) Combined and multimodal treatments in child and adolescent psychotherapy: Issues, challenges and research directions. *Clinical Psychology: Science and Practice,* 3 (1), 69-100.

Kellam, S.G., & Rebok, G.W. (1992) Building developmental and etiological theory through epidemiologically based preventive intervention trials. In J. McCord, & R.E. Tremblay (Eds.), *Preventing antisocial behaviour: Interventions from birth through adolescence,* 162-195. New York: Guilford.

Kemshall, H. (1996) *Reviewing risk. A review of research on the assessment and management of risk and dangerousness: implications for policy and practice in the Probation Service.* Home Office Research and Statistics Directorate.

Kendler, K.S., Davis, C.G., & Kessler, R.C. (1997) The familial aggregation of common psychiatric and substance use disorders in the National Comorbidity Survey: A familial history study. *British Journal of Psychiatry,* 170, 541-548.

Kessler, R.C., McGonagle, K.A., Zhao, S., Nelson, C.B., Hughes, M., Eshleman, S., Wittchen, H-U., & Kendler, S. (1994) Lifetime and 12-month prevalence of DSM-III-R psychiatric disorders in the United States. *Archives of General Psychiatry,* 51, 8-19.

Kohlberg, L. (1964) Development of moral character and moral ideology. In M.L. Hoffman & L.W. Hoffman (Eds.), *Review of Child Development Research.* 1: 383-341. New York :Russell Sage Foundation.

Kolvin, I., Miller, F.J.W., Scott, D.M., Gatzanis, S.R.M, & Fleeting, M. (1990) *Continuities of deprivation?* Aldershot: Avebury.

Kraemer, H.C., Kazdin, A.E., Offord, D.R., & Kessler, R.C. (1997) Coming to terms with the terms of risk. *Archives of General Psychiatry, 54*, 337-343.

Kratzer, L., & Hodgins, S. (1996) *A typology of offenders: A test of Moffitt's theory among males and females from childhood to age 30.* Paper presented at the Life History Research Society Meeting, London, 3-5 October.

Kroll, L., Woodham, A., Rothwell, J., Bailey, S., Tobias, C., Harrington, R., & Marshall, M. (1999) Reliability of the Salford Needs Assessment Schedule for adolescents. *Psychological Medicine, 29*, 891-902.

Kuther, T.L. & Higgins-D'Alessandro, A. (2000) Bridging the gap between moral reasoning and adolescent engagement in risky behaviour. *Journal of Adolescence, 23*, 409-422.

Lahey, B.B., Hartdagen, S.E., Frick, P.J., McBurnett, K. Connor, & Hynd, G. (1988) Conduct disorder: Parsing the confounded relation to parental divorce and antisocial personality. *Journal of Abnormal Psychology, 97*(3), 334-337.

Lahey, B.B., Waldman, I.D., & McBurnett, K. (1999) Annotation: The development of antisocial behaviour: An integrative causal model. *The Journal of Child Psychology and Psychiatry, 40*(5), 669-682.

Larzelere, R.E., & Patterson, G.R. (1990) Parental management: Mediators of the effect of socioeconomic status on early delinquency. *Criminology, 28*, 301-323.

Le Blanc, M. (1998) Screening of serious and violent juvenile offenders: Identification, classification and prediction. In R. Loeber, & D.P. Farrington (Eds.), *Serious and violent juvenile offenders: Risk factors and successful interventions,* 167-193. California: Sage Publications.

Leeman, L.W., Gibbs, J.C., & Fuller, D. (1993) Evaluation of a multicomponent group treatment programme for juvenile delinquents. *Aggressive Behaviour, 19*, 281-292.

Lewis, D.O., Shanok, S.S., Pincus, J.H., & Glaser, G.H. (1979) *Violent juvenile delinquents: Psychiatric, neurological, psychological and abuse factors.* Journal of the American Academy of Child and Adolescent Psychiatry, 18, 307-319.

Lilienfeld, S.O. (1994) Conceptual problems in the assessment of psychopathy. *Clinical Psychology Review, 14*, 17-38.

Lilienfeld, S.O., Purcell, C., & Jones-Alexander, J. (1997) Assessment of antisocial behaviour in adults. In D.M. Stoff, J. Breiling, & J.D. Maser (Eds.), *Handbook of Antisocial Behaviour,* 60-74. Chichester: Wiley.

Linehan, M. (1994) *Cognitive-behavioural treatment of borderline personality disorder.* New York: Guilford Press.

Linhorst, D.M., Hunsucker, L., & Parker, L.D. (1998) An examination of gender and racial differences among Missouri insanity acquittees. *Journal of the American Academy of Psychiatry and the Law,* 26(3), 411-424.

Lipsey, M.W. (1992) Juvenile delinquency treatment: A meta-analytic inquiry into the variability of effects. In T.D. Cook, H. Cooper, D.S. Cordray, H. Harmann, L.D. Hedges, R.J. Light, T.A. Lewis, & F. Mosteller (Eds.), *Meta-analysis for explanation: A casebook.* New York: Russell Sage.

Lipsey, M.W. (1995) What do we learn from 400 research studies on the effectiveness of treatment with juvenile delinquents? In J. McGuire (Ed.), *What works: Reducing reoffending. Guidelines from research and practice.* 63-78. Chichester: John Wiley and Sons.

Little, M., & Mount, K. (1999) *Prevention and early intervention with children in need.* Aldershot: Ashgate Publishing Company.

Loeber, R., & Farrington, D.P. (1997) Strategies and yields of longitudinal studies on antisocial behaviour. In D.M. Stoff, J. Breiling, & J.D. Maser (Eds.), *Handbook of Antisocial Behaviour,* 125-139. Chichester: Wiley.

Losel, F. (1998) Treatment and management of psychopaths. In D.J. Cooke, A.E. Forth, & R.D. Hare (Eds.) *Psychopathy: Theory, research, and implications for society.* Amsterdam:Kluwer.

Luntz, B.K., & Widom, C.S. (1994) Antisocial personality disorder in abused and neglected children grown up. *American Journal of Psychiatry,* 151(5), 670-674.

Lynam, D.R. (1996) Early identification of chronic offenders: Who is the fledgling psychopath? *Psychological Bulletin,* 120, 209-234.

McGuire, J. (Ed.) (1995). *What works: Reducing reoffending. Guidelines from research and practice.* Chichester: John Wiley and Sons.

Maguin, E., & Loeber, R. (1996) Academic performance and delinquency. In M. Tonry, & D.P. Farrington (Eds.), *Crime and Justice,* 20, 145-264. Chicago: University of Chicago Press.

Maher, M., Kelly, D. & Cook, J. (2000) *Findings and options for a Surrey-based inter-agency project for young people with complex needs.* Draft consultation paper for Surrey County Council.

Mannuzza, S., Klein, R.G., Bessler, A., Malloy, P., & LaPadula, M. (1998) Adult psychiatric status of hyperactive boys grown up. *American Journal of Psychiatry,* 155(4), 493-498.

Marshall, P. (1997) A reconviction study of HMP Grendon therapeutic community. *Research Findings 53.* Home Office Research and Statistics Directorate.

Martinson, R. (1974) What works? Questions and answers about prison reform. *The Public Interest,* 10, 22-54.

Maughan, B., Pickles, A., Hagell, A., Rutter, M., & Yule, W. (1996) *Reading problems and antisocial behaviour: Developmental trends in comorbidity.* Journal of Child Psychology and Psychiatry, 37, 405-418.

The Mental Health Foundation. (1999) *Bright futures: Promoting children and young people's mental health.* London: The Mental Health Foundation.

Milich, R.S., Hartung, C., Martin, C. & Haigler, E. (1994) Behavioural distribution and underlying processes in adolescents with disruptive behaviour disorders. In D.K Routh (Ed.), *Disruptive Behaviour Disorders in Childhood,* 109-138. New York: Plenum Press.

Miller, Q.J. (1982) *Preliminary consideration of psychological test/retest scores and their bearing upon criminal reconviction.* Grendon Psychology Unit Report, Series D, D/13.

Moffitt, T.E. (1993) Adolescence-limited and life-course-persistent antisocial behaviour: A developmental taxonomy. *Psychological Review,* 100, 674-701.

Moffitt, T.E., Caspi, A., Dickson, N., Silva, P., & Stanton, W. (1996) Childhood-onset versus adolescent-onset antisocial conduct problems in males: Natural history from ages 3 to 18 years. *Development and Psychopathology,* 9, 399-424.

Moffitt, T.E., & Silva, P.A., (1988) IQ and delinquency: A direct test of the differential detection hypothesis. *Journal of Abnormal Psychology,* 97, 330-333.

Moran, Paul. (1999) *Antisocial personality disorder. An epidemiological perspective.* London: Gaskell.

Morey, L. (1988) Personality disorders under DSM-III: An examination of convergence, and internal consistency. *American Journal of Psychiatry,* 145, 573-577.

Moyes, T., Tennent, T.G. & Bedford, A.P. (1985) Long-term follow-up of a ward based behaviour modification programme for adolescents with acting out and conduct problems. *British Journal of Psychiatry,* 147, 300-305.

Muuss, R.E. (1996) *Theories of Adolescence.* New York: McGraw Hill.

Needleman, H.L., Riess, J.A., Tobin, M.J., Biesecker, G.E., & Greenhouse, J.B. (1996) *Bone lead levels and delinquent behaviour.* Journal of the American Medical Association, 275, 363-369.

NHS/Health Advisory Service Therapeutic Review (1995) *Child and adolescent mental health services. Together we stand: The commissioning role and management of child and adolescent mental health services.* London: HMSO.

Offer, D., Ostrov, E., & Howard, K.I. (1981). *The adolescent: A psychological self-portrait.* New York: Basic Books.

Offord, D.R., Alder, R.J., & Boyle, M.H. (1986) Prevalence and socio-demographic correlates of conduct disorder. *American Journal of Social Psychiatry,* 6, 272-278.

Offord, D.R., & Reitsma-Street, M. (1983) Problems of studying antisocial behaviour. *Psychiatric Developments,* 2, 207-224.

Olweus, D. (1993) *Bullying at school: What we know and what we can do.* Oxford: Blackwell.

Olweus, D., Mattson, A., Schalling, D. & Löw, H. (1980) *Testosterone aggression, physical, and personality dimensions in normal adolescent males.* Psychosomatic Medicine, 42, 253-269.

Parker, J.G., & Asher, S.R. (1987) Peer relations and later personal adjustment: Are low-accepted children at risk? *Psychological Bulletin,* 102, 357-89.

Patterson, G.R. (1995) Coercion as a basis for early age of onset for arrest. In J. McCord, (Ed.), *Coercion and punishment in long-term perspectives*, 81-105. New York: Cambridge University Press.

Piaget, J. (1972) *The moral judgement of the child.* London: Routledge & Kegan Paul.

Power, F.C., Higgins, A., & Kohlberg, L. (1989) *Lawrence Kohlberg's approach to moral education.* New York: Columbia University Press.

Prins, H. (1991) Is psychopathic disorder a useful clinical concept? A perspective from England and Wales. *International Journal of Offender Therapy and Comparative Criminology*, 35(2), 119-125.

Pritchard, J. & Kemshall, H. (1999) *Good practice with violence.* London: Jessica Kingsley.

Pulkkinen, L. (1987) Offensive and defensive aggression in humans: A longitudinal perspective. *Aggressive Behaviour,* 13, 197-212.

Quinton, D., & Rutter, M. (1988) Parenting breakdown: *The making and breaking of inter-generational links.* Aldershot: Avebury.

Raine, A., Brennan, B., & Mednick, S.A., (1994) Birth complications combined with early maternal rejection at age 1 year predispose to violent crime at age 18 years. *Archives of General Psychiatry,* 51, 984-988.

Randall, J., Henggeler, S.W., Pickrel, S.G., & Brondino, M.J. (1999) Psychiatric comorbidity and the 16-month trajectory of substance-abusing and substance-dependent juvenile offenders. *Journal of the American Academy of Child Adolescent Psychiatry,* 38(9), 1118-1124.

Rapoport, R.N. (1960) *Community as Doctor.* London: Tavistock.

Reddy, L.A. & Pfeiffer, S.I. (1997) Effectiveness of treatment foster care with children and adolescents: A review of outcome studies. *Journal of the American Academy of Child and Adolescent Psychiatry,* 36, 581-588.

Reed, D.J. (1992) *Final Summary Report.* London: Home Office.

Reiss,D., Grubin, D., & Meux, C. (1996) Young 'psychopaths' in special hospital: Treatment and outcome. *British Journal of Psychiatry,* 168, 99-104.

Rice, M.E., Harris, G.T., & Cormier, C.A. (1992) An evaluation of a maximum security Therapeutic Community for psychopaths and other mentally disordered offenders. *Law and Human Behaviour,* 16, 399-412.

Riley, D., & Shaw, M. (1985) *Parental supervision and juvenile delinquency.* London: HMSO.

Robertson, G. & Gunn, J. (1987) A ten-year follow-up of men discharged from Grendon prison. *British Journal of Psychiatry,* 151, 674-8.

Robins, L.N. (1979) Sturdy childhood predictors of adult outcomes: Replications from longitudinal studies. In J.E. Barrett, R.M. Rose, & G.L. Klerman, (Eds.), *Stress and mental disorder,* 219-235. New York: Raven Press.

Robins, L.N. (1986) The consequences of conduct disorder in girls. In D. Olweus, J. Block, & M. Radke-Yarrow (Eds.), *Development of antisocial and prosocial behaviour: Research, theories and issues,* 385-414. Dan Diego, CA: Academic Press.

Robins, L.N., & Regier, D.A. (1991) *Psychiatric disorders in America. An ECA Study.* New York: Free Press.

Robins, L.N., Tipp, J, & Przybeck, T. (1991) Antisocial personality. In L.N. Robins & D.A. Regier, (Eds.), *Psychiatric disorders in America: The epidemiologic catchment area study,* 258-290. New York: Free Press.

Rosenkoetter, L.I., Landman, S., & Mazak, S.G. (1986) The use of moral discussion as an intervention with delinquents. *Psychological Reports,* 16, 91-94.

Rounsaville, B.J., Kranzler, H.R., Ball, S., Tennen, H., Poling, J., & Triffleman, E. (1998) Personality disorders in substance abusers: Relation to substance use. *Journal of Nervous and Mental Disease,* 186(2), 87-95.

Royal College of Psychiatrist Special Working Party on Clinical Assessment and Management of Risk (1996) *Assessment and clinical management of risk of harm to other people.* London: RCP.

Rutter, M. (1982). Psychological therapies: Issues and treatments. *Psychological Medicine,* 12, 723-40.

Rutter, M. (1989) *Psychiatric disorder in parents as a risk factor for children.* In D. Shaffer, I. Philips, N.B. Enzer, M.M. Silverman, & V. Anthony (Eds.), *Prevention of mental disorders, alcohol and other drug use in children and adolescents* (OSAP Prevention Monograph No. 2), 157-189. Rockville, MD: Office for Substance Abuse Prevention, U.S. Department of Health and Social Services.

Rutter, M. (1997) Antisocial behaviour: developmental psychopathology perspectives. In D.M. Stoff, J. Breiling, & J.D. Maser (Eds.), *Handbook of Antisocial Behaviour,* 115-124. Chichester: Wiley.

Rutter, M., Giller, H., & Hagell, A. (1998) *Antisocial behaviour by young people.* Cambridge: Cambridge University Press.

Rutter, M., Maughan, B., Meyer, J., Pickles, A., Silberg, J., Simonoff, E., & Taylor, E. (1997) Heterogeneity of antisocial behaviour: Causes, continuities, and consequences. In R. Dienstbier & D.W. Osgood (Eds.), *Nebraska symposium on motivation, vol 44: Motivation and delinquency.* Lincoln: University of Nebraska Press.

Rutter, M., & Rutter, M. (1993) *Developing minds: Challenge and continuity across the life span.* Harmondsworth: Penguin.

Rutter, M., & Smith, D.J. (Eds.) (1995) *Psychosocial disorders in young people: Time trends and their causes.* Chichester: Wiley.

Sampson, R.J., & Laub, J.H. (1993) *Crime in the making: Pathways and turning points through life.* Cambridge, MA: Harvard University Press.

Samuels, J.F., Nestadt, G., Ramanoski, A.J. et al (1994) DSM-III personality disorders in the community. *American Journal of Psychiatry,* 151, 1055-1062.

Sanderson, W.C., Wetzler, S., & Beck, A.T. et al. (1992) Prevalence of personality disorders in-patients with major depression and dysthymia. *Psychiatry Research,* 42, 93-99.

Sanford, M., Boyle, M.H., Szatmari, P., Offord, D.R., Jamieson, E., & Spinner, M. (1999) Age-of-onset classification of conduct disorder: Reliability and validity in a prospective cohort study. *Journal of the American Academy of Child Adolescent Psychiatry,* 38(3), 992.

Scott, P. (1977) Assessing dangerousness in criminals. *British Journal of Psychiatry,* 131, 127-142.

Silberg, J., Meyer, J., Pickles, A., Simonoff, E., Eaves, L., Hewitt, J., Maes, H., & Rutter, M. (1996a) Heterogeneity among juvenile antisocial behaviours: Findings from the Virginia Twin Study of Adolescent Behavioural Development. In G.R. Bock, & J.A. Goode, (Eds.), *Genetics of Criminal and Antisocial Behaviour,* (Ciba Foundation Symposium No 194), 76-85. Chichester: Wiley.

Silberg, J., Rutter, M., Meyer, J., Maes, H., Hewitt, J., Simonoff, E., Pickles, A., Loeber, R., & Eaves, L. (1996b) Genetic and environmental influences of the covariation between hyperactivity and conduct disturbance in juvenile twins. *Journal of Child Psychology and Psychiatry,* 37, 803-816.

Silverthorn, P., & Frick, P.J. (1999) Developmental pathways to antisocial behaviour: The delayed-onset pathway in girls. *Development and Psychopathology,* 11, 101-126.

Simon, L.M.J. (1998) Does criminal offender treatment work? *Applied and Preventative Psychology,* 7, 137-159.

Singleton, N., Meltzer, H., Gatward, R., Coid, J., & Deasy, D. (1998) *Psychiatric morbidity among prisoners in England and Wales.* London: The Stationery Office.

Skuse, D., Bentovim, A. et al. (1999) *Sexually abusive behaviour in males: Origins and development.* Conference given at Institute of Child Health, Great Ormond Street Hospital, 30 September 1999.

Spence, S.H., & Marzillier, J.S. (1981) Social skills training with adolescent male offenders: 11. Short-term, long-term, and generalised effects. *Behaviour Research and Therapy,* 19, 349-368.

Spitzer, R.L., & Williams, J.B.W. (1987) *Structured clinical interview for DSM-III-R personality disorders (SCID-II).* New York State Psychiatric Institute, Biometric Research Department.

Steinberg, D. (1994) Adolescent services. In M., Rutter, E. Taylor, & I. Hersov (Eds.), *Child and Adolescent Services: Modern Approaches.* Oxford: Blackwell Scientific Publications.

Steiner, H., Cauffman, E., & Duxbury, E. (1999) Personality traits in juvenile delinquents: Relation to criminal behaviour and recidivism. *Journal of the American Academy of Child Adolescent Psychiatry,* 38(3), 256-262.

Stevens, G.F. (1993) Applying the diagnosis antisocial personality to imprisoned offenders: Looking for hay in a haystack. *Journal of Offender Rehabilitation,* 19, 1-26.

Stewart, M.A., & Leone, L. (1978) A family study of unsocialized aggressive boys. *Biological Psychiatry,* 13(1), 107-117.

Stoff, D.M., Breiling, J., & Maser, J.D. (Eds.) (1997) *Handbook of antisocial behaviour.* Chichester: Wiley.

Strupp, H.H., & Hadley, S.W. (1979) Specific versus nonspecific factors in psychotherapy: A controlled study of outcome. *Archives of General Psychiatry,* 36, 1125-1136.

Stuart, S., Pfohl, B., Battaglia, M., Bellodi, L., Grove, W., & Cadoret, R. (1998) The co-occurrence of DSM-III-R personality disorders. *Journal of Personality Disorder,* 12, 302-315.

Sullivan, P.F., Wells, J.E., & Bushnell, J.A. (1995) Adoption as a risk factor for mental disorders. *Acta Psychiatrica Scandinavica,* 92(2), 119-124.

Swanson, M.C.J., Bland, R.C., & Newman, S.C. (1994) Antisocial personality disorders. *Acta Psychiatrica Scandinavica,* (Suppl. 376), 63-70.

Taylor, A.J.W. (1967) An evaluation of group psychotherapy in a girls' borstal. *International Journal of Group Psychotherapy,* 17, 168-177.

Taylor, E. (1991) Toxins and allergens. In M. Rutter & P. Casaer (Eds.), *Biological risk factors for psychosocial disorders,* 199-232. Cambridge: Cambridge University Press.

Tolan, P.H., & Gorman-Smith, D. (1997) Treatment of juvenile delinquency: between punishment and therapy. In D.M. Stoff, J. Breiling, & J.D. Maser (Eds.), *Handbook of antisocial behaviour,* 405-415. Chichester: Wiley.

Tonry, M. and Farrington, D.P. (1995) Strategic approaches to crime prevention. In M. Tonry and D.P. Farrington (Eds) *Building a Safer Society: Strategic approaches to crime prevention.* Chicago: University of Chicago Press.

Tremblay, R.E., Pihl, R.O., Vitaro, F., & Dobkin, P.L. (1994) Predicting early onset of male antisocial behaviour from pre-school behaviour. *Archives of General Psychiatry,* 51, 732-9.

Trevethan, S.D. & Walker, L.J. (1989) Hypothetical versus real-life moral reasoning among psychopathic and delinquent youth. *Development and Psychopathology,* 1, 91-103.

Truax, C.B., Wargo, D.G., & Silber, L.D. (1966) Effects of group psychotherapy with high adequate empathy and nonpossessive warmth upon female institutionalised delinquents. *Journal of Abnormal Psychology,* 71, 267-274.

Tuinier, S., Verhoeven, W.M.A., & van Praag, H.M. (1995) *Cerebrospinal fluid 5-hydroxyindolacetic acid and aggression: A critical reappraisal of the clinical data.* International Clinical Psychopharmacology, 10, 147-156.

Tweed, J.L., George, L.K., Blazer, D., Swartz, M. et al (1994) Adult onset of severe and pervasive antisocial behaviour: A distinct syndrome, *Journal of Personality Disorders,* 8:3, 192-202.

Villani, S., & Sharfstein, S.S. (1999) Evaluating and treating violent adolescents in the managed care era. *American Journal of Psychiatry,* 156(3), 458-464.

von Bertalanffy, L. (1968) *General systems theory.* New York: Braziller.

Walker, M.A. (1995) *Interpreting crime statistics.* Oxford: Clarendon.

Walters, G.D. (1990) *The criminal lifestyle: Patterns of serious criminal conduct.* Newbury Park, CA: Sage.

Washington State Institute for Public Policy (1998) *Watching the bottom line: Cost-effective interventions for reducing crime in Washington.* Internet publication at: http:/www.wa.gov/wsipp/reports/bline.html.

Webster-Stratton, C. & Hammond, M. (1997) Treating children with early-onset conduct problems: A comparison of child and parent training interventions. *Journal of Consulting and Clinical Psychology,* 65, 93-109.

Weiss, G., Hechtman, L., Milroy, T., & Perlman, T. (1985) Psychiatric status of hyperactives as adults: A controlled prospective 15-year follow-up of 63 hyperactive children. *Journal of the American Academy of Child Psychiatry,* 24(2), 211-220.

West, D.J., & Farrington, D.P. (1973) *Who becomes delinquent?* London: Heinemann.

West, D.J., & Farrington, D.P. (1977) *The delinquent way of life.* London: Heinemann.

Weinberger, D. (1997) Distress and self-restraint as measures of adjustment across the life span: confirmatory factor analysis in clinical and nonclinical samples. *Psychological Assessment,* 9, 132-135.

Wilson, G.T. (1997) Treatment manuals in clinical practice. *Behaviour Research and Therapy,* 35, 205-210.

Wootton, J.M., Frick, P.J., Shelton, K.K., & Silverthorn, P. (1997) Callous-unemotional traits and conduct problems: A two-factor model of psychopathy in children. *Issues in Criminological and Legal Psychology,* 24, 47-51.

World Health Organisation. (1993) ICD-10. *The ICD-10 classification of mental and behavioural disorders. Diagnostic criteria for research.* Geneva: World Health Organisation.

Yates, W.R., Petty, F., & Brown, K. (1988) Alcoholism in males with antisocial personality disorder. *International Journal of the Addictions,* 23(10), 999-1010.

Yoshikawa, H. (1994) Prevention as cumulative protection: Effects of early family support and education on chronic delinquency and its risks. *Psychological Bulletin,* 115,128-54.

RDS Publications

Requests for Publications

Copies of our publications and a list of those currently available may be obtained from:

> Home Office
> Research, Development and Statistics Directorate
> Communications Development Unit
> Room 201, Home Office
> 50 Queen Anne's Gate
> London SW1H 9AT
> Telephone: 020 7273 2084 (answerphone outside of office hours)
> Facsimile: 020 7222 0211
> E-mail: publications.rds@homeoffice.gsi.gov.uk

alternatively

why not visit the RDS website at
>   Internet: http://www.homeoffice.gov.uk/rds/index.html

where many of our publications are available to be read on screen or downloaded for printing.